BRAIN RECOVERY

A Journey of Hope

How a learning mindset helps create new neural pathways after a stroke.

BY LAURA STOICESCU

ISBN

978-1-7386-3200-8 (paperback)

978-1-7386320-1-5 (eBook)

To Dumitru—my love, soulmate,
life partner, and best advocate

PREFACE

I had spent a beautiful weekend in Whistler, BC, cross-country skiing with Dumitru, my husband, and a couple of friends. We had a great time, with sunny skies and the occasional soft snow shower. Then it was time to get back to reality as I had a hectic week ahead of me. On the evening of Wednesday, February 6, 2019, I was not feeling well, so I went to bed early. The following day, I woke up in the hospital. I had suffered a spontaneous carotid and vertebral artery dissection the night before, resulting in a major stroke. It would take me months to understand what that meant, what the recovery required of me to get back to "normal," what it took to figure out how to navigate the healthcare system in Canada, and how long it would take to find the necessary support needed to facilitate my healing.

I had lost the ability to read, spell, and write. My right hand and arm were paralyzed, and I could not hold a pen. Three years later, after a lot of hard work and determination, I have written this book. This is my story of recovery, my journey of hope and strength.

CONTENTS

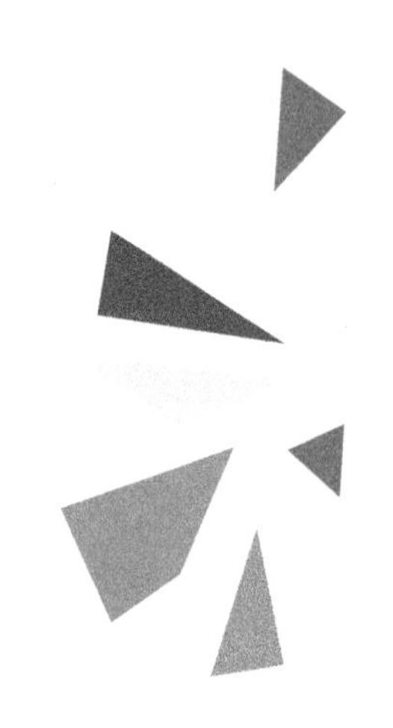

INTRODUCTION

FEBRUARY 6, 2019

Wednesday

I lived in Tsawwassen, a small-town South of Vancouver, BC, Canada, and worked as a Technology Manager at a large utility company. I anticipated a busy day at work, including a monthly meeting with an expected forty-five of my colleagues in attendance. I started the day early in the morning, attended various conference calls, then spent forty-five minutes in heavy traffic, driving from downtown to participate in the project managers' meeting on the other side of the city. My job included training and developing project management methodologies. On that day, I facilitated a complex session, then left work and looked forward to working out at the gym.

I was born in communist Romania, where it was mandatory for high school students to take part in a working practicum in a noisy factory. I had suffered two very intense migraine attacks—aura, nausea, and head pain as a teenager. I could not handle any smells, light, or noise and felt sick for a few days after each spell. Both attacks happened when I was in high school.

After my second migraine attack at the age of seventeen, my doctor exempted me from the factory work practicum and allowed me to complete it in a small workshop in the school building instead. This was unusual as the Romanian communist regime did not take kindly to pupils being excused from mandatory school/factory work.

Over time, I experienced several migraines in my thirties and forties until June 2018, when I began to experience an increase in the number of migraines and headaches I was having. My family doctor sent me for a CT scan but found nothing. In September 2018, I suffered the worse migraine to date. I woke up at night suddenly, with my head throbbing. I was very dizzy and nauseous. Taking an Advil or a migraine pill was no use, as even thinking of sipping water made me throw up. In hindsight, I should have called 911. I was home alone and assumed it would pass, even though I was in agony for hours.

Back to the Gym

I attended my regular one-hour group workout, but minutes before the class finished, something happened; the vision in both my eyes became affected. I could see, but I could not see properly. I suddenly had double-vision, and a strange feeling overtook me as though my eyes had to constantly re-adjust to see correctly. I took my glasses off and put them back on several times to see if my eyes would adjust but to no avail. Nothing else felt wrong. I managed to finish the class and then drove home. By the time I arrived, I had assumed I was having a migraine attack, though I had no headache. Before dinner, I told my husband, Dumitru, that I had to take an Advil and lie down for a few minutes, which had never happened before. Once in bed, I closed my eyes, and that was the last thing I remembered.

FEBRUARY 7, 2019
Thursday

I woke up in a bright room. Since I was a child, I have worn prescription glasses for myopia. In communist Romania, contact lenses were unavailable, and I later discovered that lenses did not help me much as my prescription changed every year. So, not having my glasses by my side when I awoke was disturbing. However, Dumitru was there, and he helped put my glasses on. I looked around and saw a man and a woman. There was a computer in the room, and the man was watching the screen. The woman came toward me and spoke, saying I was experiencing a bad headache, but I could not understand what she was saying. Later, Dumitru told me that he had disclosed to them that I had been at the gym before coming home the previous evening. I could not hear nor process much of the information. I remember staying in bed, hooked up to machines. The man and woman came in and out of my room several times that day. I remember the man looked very serious, and the woman spoke in a soothing and kind voice.

FEBRUARY 8, 2019

Friday

I woke up the next day in the same room. I remember sleeping, then being woken up to drink a mysterious liquid and take a pill. I was now aware that the man and woman I had seen the other day were doctors—a neurologist and a resident doctor. The resident doctor reassured me that my headache was getting better. I then realized that I felt no pain, which was odd. I also realized that I was in the ICU and must be quite ill, but I was too tired to think. Dumitru was by my side every time I woke up, so I felt safe.

FEBRUARY 9, 2019

Saturday

Talks of being moved from the ICU to a private room began. I was now aware of the nurses coming in and out, who were friendly and kind. They would often come to see me and ask simple questions, such as my name, where I was, the date, etc. I was too tired to answer most of the time, but I tried, partly because I am polite and partly because I wanted to know why they were asking such simple questions.

Earlier that day, a friendly face arrived that I recognized (maybe from the previous day?). She had a positive energy about her—always smiling and upbeat but gentle. She was the neurology physiotherapist. She talked to Dumitru and me about the importance of moving my arm and hand. I did not understand what she was saying. However, I noticed that my right arm and right hand looked different. How strange; I felt nothing. What was wrong with my right arm and hand? I was too tired to ask. I remember her saying they would soon transfer me to a private room.

After lunch that day, someone helped me out of bed and moved me to a wheelchair. They said the wheelchair was too big for me, but it would do for the move. I began to understand that something was wrong with my right side. I could not process what was happening as I was distracted by the number of people in the room—the neurologist, the resident, the physiotherapist, Dumitru, and the nurses. They moved me from the ICU to a private room. I was tired; all I wanted was to sleep, but a nurse brought me to the bathroom and helped me wash my hands. What was wrong with my hand? My arm? I looked in the bathroom mirror and began to cry. I collapsed, and several people rushed into the room, lifting me onto the bed. Then everything went blank.

The events and information about what had happened before and after my collapse were pieced together slowly over the following days, weeks, and months. From what I understood, I had initially suffered a spontaneous internal carotid and vertebral artery dissection on my left side, possibly due to a genetic condition called fibromuscular dysplasia. This apparently caused a major stroke, although I do not recall hearing the word "stroke" while I was in the hospital. From what I understand, I believe the doctors were hoping that my body would recover without surgery. That was likely why I was initially held in the ICU for two to three days before being deemed stable enough to move to a private room. However, after I collapsed as I was getting settled, the decision was made to go ahead with the surgery. I was not aware of any discussions about my choices at that time.

The doctors at Vancouver General Hospital (VGH) gave Dumitru several options, and he later told me that the first option was bad and the second even worse. This was due to the position of my arteries, making it difficult for the neurosurgeon to place the necessary stents. After Dumitru signed off on the surgery, he waited more than seven hours before being told that the surgery had been a success.

I vaguely remember the next ICU room in which they had placed me. I was aware of my surroundings a few times; Dumitru was there, and the nurses continued to ask me tiresome questions and moved my arms and legs.

FEBRUARY 14, 2019

Thursday

I was released from the ICU and moved to a shared room. The routine was similar. A nurse came every four hours, asking the same questions: "What is your name?" "Where are you?" "What is today's date?" I knew how to say my name and give the location of the hospital. However, I was having trouble with the date. I knew it was February, but it was challenging to figure out the day and year. Why could I not say the correct numbers? I could picture the numbers in my head, but the wrong sounds came out.

Often, doctors, nurses, and others surrounded my bed, and Dumitru was not allowed in the room when they were there. The questions would come in short succession: "Were you aware that you had fibromuscular dysplasia?" "Does anyone in your family have it?" I heard comments about hypermobility of the fingers and joints; I heard many terms that I did not understand. I was aware of my surroundings and tried to absorb as much information as possible. I remember speaking very little, but I spoke English when I did. However, I rarely answered their questions because I was often exhausted and mainly because it felt like everything was happening in slow-motion, and I could not comprehend it fast enough to respond.

Nonetheless, I had much bigger issues to worry about. The shared room had five or six beds, with patients coming in and out constantly. The first night in this room was unpleasant. I remember all the patients. There was an elderly lady who was confused and frightened and a young lady with severe issues with her eyesight, waiting to be transported by plane. The elderly lady often woke up crying, while the girl complained of being dizzy. I felt terrible for them and wanted to comfort them. I could not understand why they weren't getting any help, not realizing that I was myself drifting in and out of sleep throughout the night.

By the end of the second day, I was crying almost all the time. I could not explain to Dumitru what was wrong. He talked to the doctors, and a psychiatry doctor and a resident came to see me. They asked Dumitru to wait outside. The doctor spoke to me briefly about the fact that sadness was normal. He then left, and the resident began to ask me questions: "Do you feel suicidal?" "Would you consider medication?" I was stunned. What was he talking about? I was not sad; I was fine. I just wanted them to stop asking me questions and instead help the others in the room who needed support. I felt I needed to do something to ease their distress, but I could not say the words, so I started crying instead.

When Dumitru came back into the room, he brought my iPod with him. Having music on helped to block out the noise and calmed me down. He told the doctors and nurses that my issue was not sadness, insisting they move me to a room with fewer patients and less noise. He worked hard to convince the administrators to find a solution as I was getting worse by the hour. The next day, they moved me to a small private room.

FEBRUARY 16, 2019
Saturday

I was now receiving daily abdominal injections of medication to help prevent blood clots. I remember sitting in a wheelchair by the window, watching the seagulls and crows outside when a nurse came in and noticed blood on my shirt but no sign of a cut. The injection I was given was causing the bleeding. The nurse placed bandages on my abdomen, and I endured a restless night as nurses continually came in to dress my injection site. Eighteen hours later, the doctors decided to stop the injections and suggested I walk instead to prevent blood clots from forming, provided I was committed to staying active.

Dumitru came the next morning, and we began our daily walks. Before my hospitalization, I was very fit. I had completed seven half-marathons, three 14 km races, and many 10 km and 5 km races. I worked out at the gym four to five times per week, ran once or twice per week (3–5 km runs), and practiced yoga once per week. I enjoyed playing tennis with Dumitru and other couples in the spring, summer, and fall. In winter, I downhill and cross-country skied. Being active always gave me a sense of purpose, whether to support charity runs or help with stress relief, and now I had found something familiar again. I was already looking forward to the daily hand physiotherapist exercises, so the doctors' recommendation to walk daily was great news for me!

To keep track of my steps, I wanted to use my phone. Unfortunately, I could not remember my passcode. In the end, Dumitru used his Notes and later unlocked my phone for me.

Notes from my phone after walking in the hallways:

- February 19, 2019: 7:30 a.m.; 9:00 a.m.; 10:00 a.m.—one lap from my room to the nurses' station (20–30 meters)

- February 20, 2019: 8:00 a.m.; 9:15 a.m.; 10:00 a.m.; 11:00 a.m.; 12:30 p.m.; 2:00 p.m.; 3:00 p.m.—two laps from my room to the end of the hallway (60–70 meters)

- February 21, 2019: 8:00 a.m. (2 laps); 9:00 a.m. (2 laps); 10:00 a.m. (2 laps); assessments; 12:30 p.m. (2 laps); 1:20 p.m. (1 lap); 2:30 p.m. (2 laps); 4:45 p.m. (3 laps); 6:00 p.m. (3 laps); 6:40 p.m. (3 laps)

FEBRUARY 22, 2019

Friday

On Friday afternoon, almost two weeks after my surgery, around 3 p.m., Dumitru had to leave early for a meeting.

Not long after that, a nurse told me I would be moved to another hospital closer to home, which surprised and upset me as she gave me no warning. I heard the nurse telling me that I was being moved to the Surrey Memorial Hospital. I knew where that was and did not understand why I was to be moved there as it was even further away from our home. I had my iPhone but did not know how to dial Dumitru's number to let him know I was leaving suddenly. I still had difficulty remembering the day of the week, let alone phone numbers. Fortunately, I recognized the iMessage icon, and Dumitru's name came up. I managed to text him that I was being moved, but I could hardly spell, which further confused me. Dumitru texted me back, saying he would call Vancouver General Hospital and meet me at the second hospital that night.

Not having Dumitru with me when they transported me to Surrey Memorial was hard on me. He had been by my bedside constantly for the last couple of weeks; he was there when I woke up and there when I went to sleep in the evening. I felt that I was on my own and no longer in control of what was happening to me. They placed me on a special stretcher/wheelchair, and I remember that the medical transport driver was nice, but I did not know him. He asked me about my Romanian accent, but he did not realize I had difficulty speaking and processing so much information. Traffic was busy, it was snowing and dark, and I did not recognize the streets. I was tired, and I wanted to go to sleep.

Surrey Memorial Hospital was big, dark, and far away from home, and the nurses were unfamiliar, so I shut down. Dumitru came late that evening and was not allowed to stay long. A female doctor eventually came to see me after midnight, waking me up to ask questions. I was half-asleep, and her questions went unanswered. I was exhausted, and soon after, drifted off to sleep again.

FEBRUARY 23, 2019

Saturday

The next day started with understanding my new surroundings. Dumitru came early in the morning, and I felt much better. We resumed our laps.

A team of therapists came in to complete an assessment. I was asked to count down from 100 in increments of 7. I thought this was strange, but I was used to being asked strange questions by now. I took my time to answer, and after reaching 58, I was told I had passed the test. The next assessment was about safety, to confirm that my reasoning was sound—what would I do if a fire broke out, who would I call first, etc. Another assessment was about my posture and ability to use my arms and legs. By that time, the therapist realized I was doing very well with walking. My right hand, wrist, and arm were paralyzed, but my legs were fine. I was asked to walk up and down a few steps and a ramp, and the therapist checked my posture as I followed her instructions—step forward, step backward, go faster, go slower, stop, etc. Since the instructions were verbal and the therapist demonstrated each one first, I found it easy. After my assessment, the consensus was that I could be released from the hospital as Dumitru would be there to help. I was so excited to go home!

As a final test, the team of therapists asked me to use my left hand to type a few words to see how I could manage typing reminders, shopping notes, etc., as my right (dominant) arm was paralyzed. Although I was slow in my interaction with the therapists, doctors, and nurses, I was precise in my answers, and my communication was fine. By now, they knew a few things about me: I spoke English very well, I was an information technology manager, and I was very familiar with computers. One of the therapists brought in a laptop and asked me to type my name using my left hand. I was very confident. I started: L...La...La... I did not understand. Of course, I knew my name! My name was Laura. My name is spelled the same in English and Romanian but is pronounced differently. I tried again. L...La...Lo...I could not get past the first two letters. Something was wrong. The therapist realized I had lost the ability to spell. We did not do any more tests as I was in shock. I do not remember much about the rest of the day.

FEBRUARY 24, 2019
Sunday

I was released from the hospital the next day, with a set of occupational therapy exercises to do at home: elbow flexion palm facing toward, then away; elbow extensions; wrist flexion and extension; wrist radial deviation; wrist circles; trying to make a tent with the fingers as the palm is faced down; thumb movement in and out; and finger peeling. The therapist also recommended several clinics if I wanted to pursue private sessions while waiting to receive occupational therapy and speech therapy from the hospital.

As we drove home along the snowy streets, I read the street signs passing us by. In hindsight, I most likely recognized the logos and not the actual words. However, I was too tired to realize it then. When we got home, I went straight to bed and slept until the next morning.

FEBRUARY 25–27, 2019
Monday–Wednesday

The first days at home were strange. I felt very fragile, and everything took me a long time. One day, I fainted as I got out of the shower, and we later learned that my blood pressure was being heavily controlled to keep my heart rate down for the stent recovery process to occur. Taking a shower took half an hour, and by the end of it, I was ready to go back to bed. Dumitru prepared all the meals as I could not stay awake for more than one hour at a time.

We immediately started my daily walking routine as we knew I had to walk every few hours. First, we walked to the end of the driveway and back; then, we walked to the end of the street and back. Within weeks, I could walk slowly for 30 minutes per day, which helped since my mind was now starting to wake up, and I was slowly beginning to process what had happened.

PHYSICAL RECOVERY

The following chapters describe in more detail the physical aspect of my recovery. My brain recovery was not linear but weaving through as things progressed over the following weeks, months, and years. However, I recognize that it was easier for me to focus first on my physical recovery. It was easier for me to understand what was needed to regain my physical form and the functioning of my arm. I started journaling to keep track of my physical progress. Only more than a year later, I decided to document my emotional recovery.

OCCUPATIONAL THERAPY

MARCH–MAY 2019

Occupational therapy is a form of therapy that encourages rehabilitation through activities required in daily life for those recuperating from physical and mental illnesses.

In March 2019, I was referred to the Peace Arch Hospital, a small outpatient hospital in a community unfamiliar to me, where we had to wait to get an appointment to meet with an occupational therapist. On the first assessment with the occupational therapist, we were told about the "strike three, you're out" policy, meaning I could not miss sessions. I immediately tensed up. Although I know this was unintentional, it made me feel like an afraid, guilty child that had done something wrong. I knew that I still needed many other medical appointments at Vancouver General Hospital in the following months, so the fear that I might be kicked out of the outpatient program because of missed appointments frightened me.

The occupational therapist's first focus was my right arm and hand, as I could not feel my hand or fingers. I had started to feel my elbow when I was still at the Vancouver General Hospital (14–15 days after the stent surgery). I began to feel my wrist on the last day of being released from the Surrey Memorial Hospital. We asked the occupational therapist about hand physiotherapy, as the physiotherapist at VGH advised us to start therapy right away. At Peace Arch Hospital, we were told that I would not need any other rehabilitation therapy other than occupational therapy. They told us that the occupational therapy would address my needs, with 10 minutes of the 45 minutes allocated for my right arm and hand at every session. Furthermore, we were told that they do not encourage patients to combine outpatient therapy with private hand physiotherapy as the practitioners use different methods that may confuse patients. I followed the physical instructions, strength measurements, checks on testing the sensations of hot/cold and the ability to feel anything in my right palm and fingers (there was no sensation at all at that time).

The occupational therapist's second focus was my reasoning. I was asked to follow some written and oral directions, in the same assessment. However, I needed time and felt slow. I could not write. I felt uncomfortable being watched and corrected; I was very self-conscious. I did not do well with certain oral directions or when I was shown things on paper. Shading in a circle was easy, but underlining a rectangle was more difficult. Even though I understood the shapes, I did not understand what underlining or writing above a shape meant. Putting a dot in a circle was also easy but putting a dot under the circle had no meaning. I felt very discouraged. I was even more discouraged because I did not understand why I could not do these things, and the occupational therapist offered no explanation.

When I finished the assessment, the occupational therapist reminded me that the outpatient hospital took things very seriously and that I was not to miss any sessions. I was stressed that I would be thrown out of the outpatient services if I did something wrong. I was so afraid that I decided against telling them that we had already started private hand physiotherapy sessions while waiting.

Over the next three months, I had three to four individual occupational therapy sessions, and then I was asked to participate in a series of six group sessions. Each session was about 45 minutes long. It was fascinating to see patients at different levels of recovery. I was the patient with the most recent brain injury. I was exhausted after each session and continued to be very self-conscious. My dexterity improved fast as I had three private hand physiotherapy sessions every week. However, I still did not have any strength in my fingers, hand, or wrist.

While I was progressing well with the private hand physiotherapy, I did not feel that I was benefitting as much from the outpatient occupational therapy sessions. I felt uncomfortable with the lack of explanation when things were not working for me. I needed to understand why certain things were hard and what I could do to improve them. In the end, we decided not to continue with outpatient occupational therapy.

It is important to note that finding your way through recovery is very personal. The following chapters will show that my occupational therapy journey at the Peace Arch Hospital was relatively short and not as successful as my other recovery journeys. Circumstances, background and history, individual style, and patient-therapist connections all contribute to allowing one to find what works best for them. I came across occupational therapy again during my GRASP journey (to be discussed in a later chapter). As I was dealing with many other health challenges over the spring and summer of 2019, I was likely not ready to tackle occupational therapy at the beginning. Many of the things I did not understand in March 2019 made sense in January 2020. The key for patients and their families is not to give up and continue to find the occupational therapy programs and therapists that are right for them. Find the right person, the right program, and the right location that suits your needs, and you will be rewarded with positive results in the end.

PHYSIOTHERAPY

FEBRUARY 2019

I met Erin, my hand physiotherapist, on February 28, 2019. I remember walking into her office and immediately getting onto a stationary bike for a few minutes to warm up. My hands were very cold. Erin had to keep adjusting my right hand as I could not hold onto the handlebar.

I learned so much from my first session:

- I learned to use a small electric pillow to warm up my hands before exercises.

- I learned to stretch my wrist as my fingers were getting very tight. I started to exercise my wrist by spreading my fingers over a tennis ball and lifting my wrist. I could not hold onto the ball, so we had to wrap a piece of fabric and an elastic to keep my hand in the correct position to lift my wrist. The therapist talked about the small muscles that needed to be worked on.

- I learned about correcting my right hand and arm position as I had forgotten about them because I did not feel them. I was told to keep my right hand on my knee and stay aware of my body position when I sat.

- I learned tenting exercises and lifting my fingers up and down to engage my intrinsic muscles. At first, I could only move my fingers a little bit off the table, more like a flicker, as the therapist worked my hand and fingers. I understood the idea, and because I knew the importance of continually stimulating my brain, I was eager to try.

- The therapist used a muscle stimulation device, and I began to feel my fingers move, especially the thumb and index, as they felt numb. The neuromuscular stimulation device is used to prevent disuse atrophy, relax muscle spasms, aid in muscle re-education, and increase muscle range of motion. The therapist attached a series of electrode pads connected to the device to my right wrist and the base of my thumb or the back of my right palm. The therapist would then control the intensity of the electrical stimulation to exercise the muscle.

We agreed with Erin to embark on an intense hand therapy program as I wanted to see results fast. By then, several medical professionals had told me that recovery could only occur during the first few months; after that, I would be left with whatever impairments I could not correct in time. Their intent may have been to motivate people from the get-go, and some practitioners may genuinely believe that recovery is not possible after a few months, but this does not have to be the case!

We went home excited after the session with Erin and started practicing every day. I felt good—now I had a plan!

MARCH 6, 2019

10 to 12 Hand Therapy Sessions in March

On March 6, 2019, I was happy to show Erin my progress in the second session. My right wrist was already in a much better position, and I could lift the tennis ball using a lighter wrap to keep my hand in place (Fig. 1). Furthermore, I learned to hold a playing card in my left hand and slowly pull the card with my right hand (Fig. 2). The goal was to pinch the card between my right thumb and index fingers. We also brought a small pepper grinder from home to show Erin that I could grasp it and move it a few inches away. Erin added exercises to build on wrist rotations—left, right, up, down—mimicking the motion of pouring tea from a teapot. I then learned to grasp an empty cup and practiced bringing the cup to my mouth (Fig. 3). I also learned how to "teach" my right hand to do things

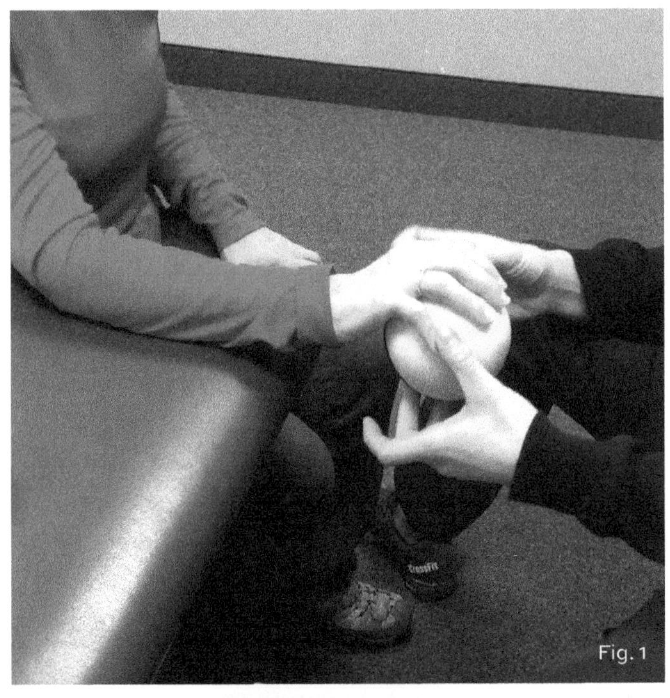
Fig. 1

Fig. 2

Fig. 3

by "showing" how my left hand did them, mimicking the motion with my right hand. Lastly, I learned the difference between squeezing, grabbing, and pinching something, using different muscles for each action.

I had to remember to use my hand all the time! Practice, practice, practice! Erin said that my brain would re-learn how to do things through constant repetition.

I was so thrilled with my progress and how many improvements I had made in less than a week that I began to look forward to my next sessions.

MARCH 8, 2019

On this day, we honoured *Women's Day*. In Romania, Women's Day is highly celebrated; it's the equivalent of Mother's Day. Typically, Dumitru and I would throw a party with flowers and gifts, but we opted for a quiet dinner at home this year instead. Dumitru bought me a bouquet and some "toys" to help with my recovery, including plastic cups, cubes, dice, dominos, playing cards, small and big balls, etc.

Earlier that afternoon, Dumitru and I went for a walk and ran into a couple of tennis friends. They did not know what had happened to me, and I did not want anyone to know. They asked if we were looking forward to playing tennis, and, as usual, Dumitru did most of the talking. I was very aware of my right arm; it felt like dead weight. I was wearing mittens, as I was always cold. However, I could not put them on myself; Dumitru helped for months. I was terrified that my friends would notice that my right arm was paralyzed. I did not realize it at the time, but most people did not notice anything.

MARCH 11–27, 2019
More Hand Therapy Sessions

As I continued with hand therapy, the exercises became more difficult.

I started to learn how to shuffle cards—I was not successful. Instead of shuffling them, I would place one card on the table at a time (Fig. 4-5). I also tried to stack dominos (Fig. 6), rotating them in different positions, but I found it very challenging. Once I mastered this, I was told to add erasers on top of the dominos, then small dice.

Erin showed me how to roll putty to make a log (Fig. 7), place clothespins onto a bowl (Fig. 8), and stack coins. These exercises were challenging as I had no strength in my arm and wrist, and my right fingers were very tight and swollen.

I had to learn to stretch them, so I continued doing tenting exercises and began to master flipping cards and to play with cubes—rotating them in my palm.

Next, I mastered making small putty balls, lining them up on the table, placing them into a plastic cup, then placing cards on top of the cups (Fig. 9–10).

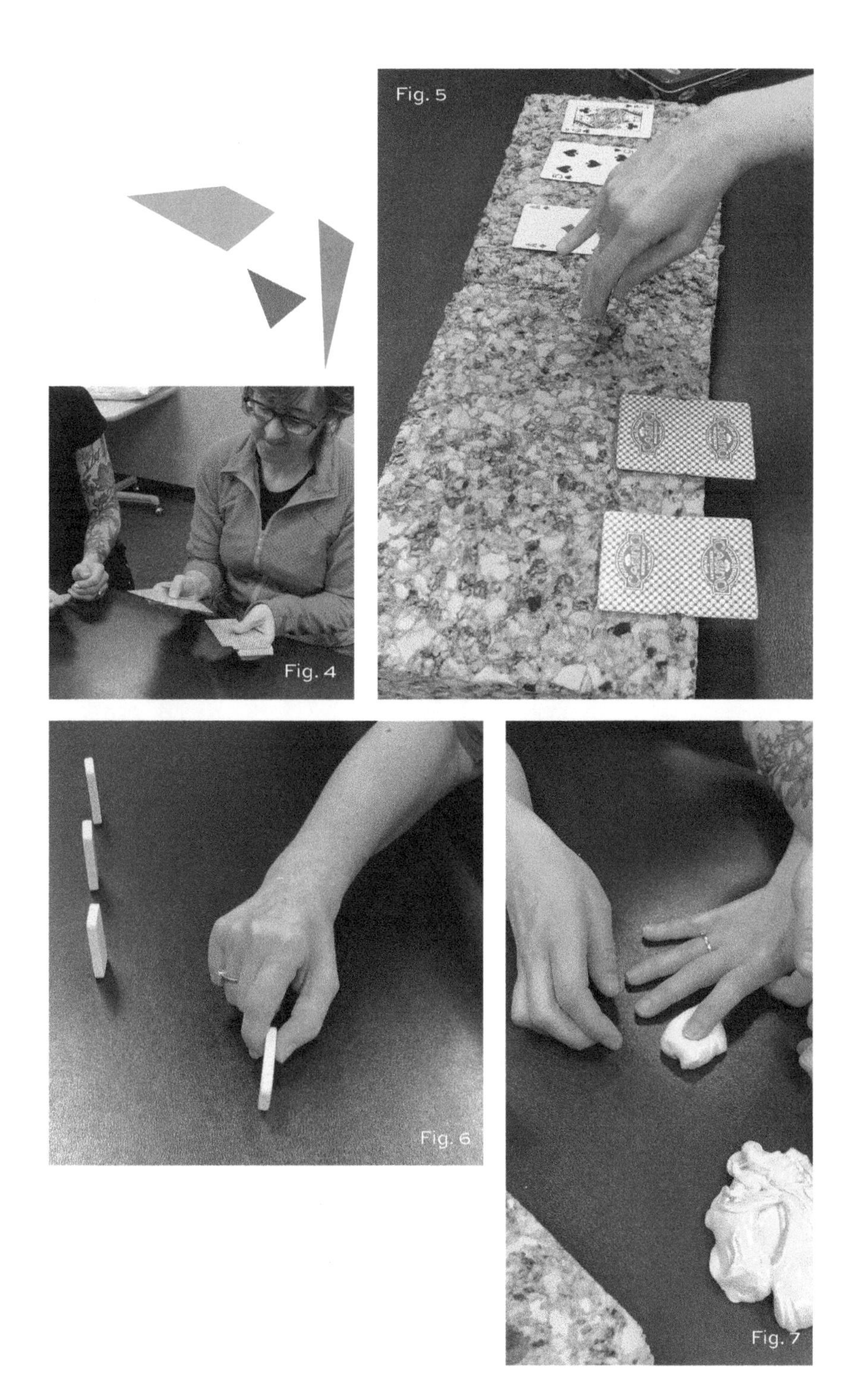
Fig. 5
Fig. 4
Fig. 6
Fig. 7

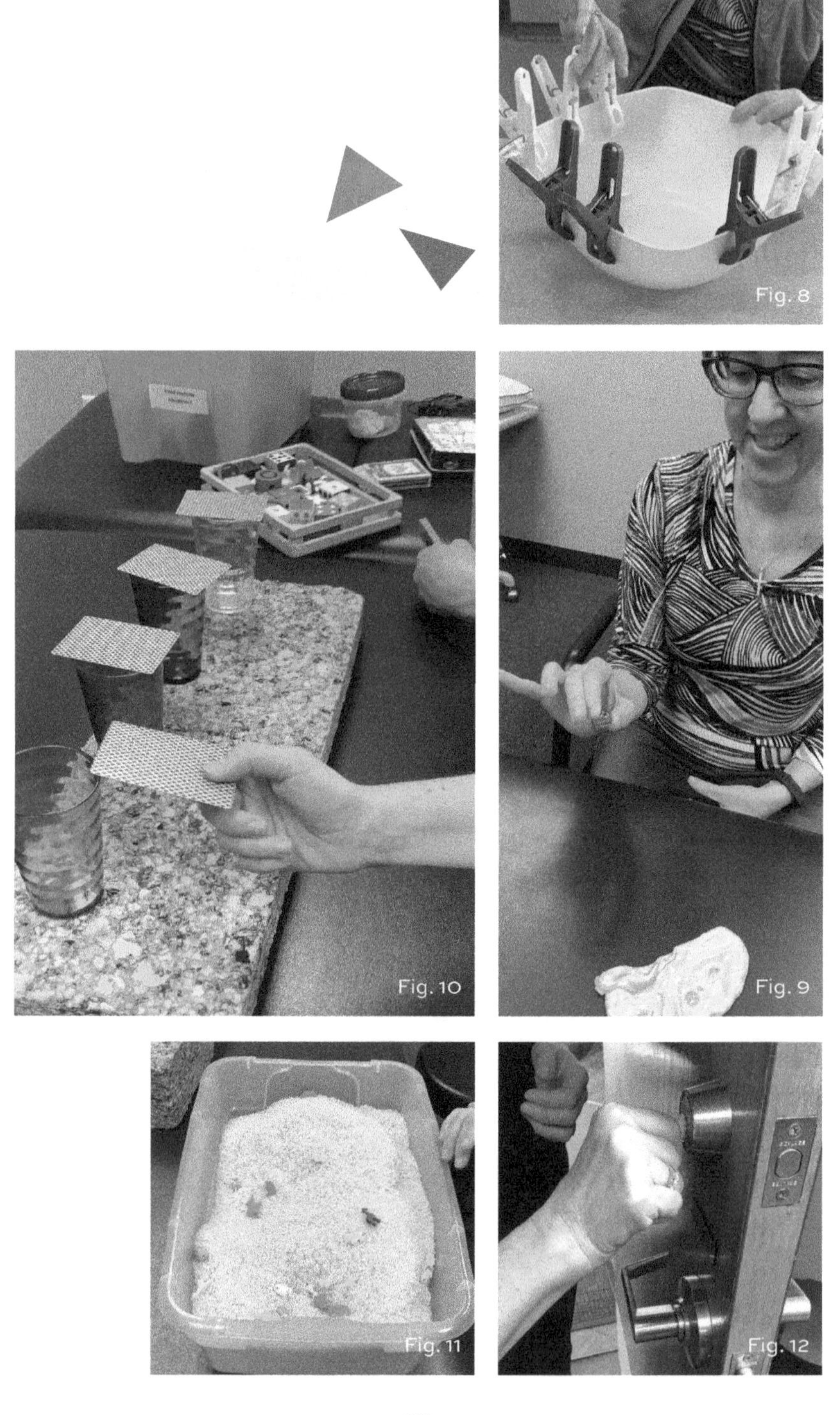

Fig. 8

Fig. 10

Fig. 9

Fig. 11

Fig. 12

Erin then taught me tactile exercises, which were discouraging because I could not feel my fingers. The exercises involved placing my hand into a box of rice and feeling around for hidden objects within (Fig. 11). At first, I could not feel anything. I gradually started to feel the objects after several attempts, but I could not distinguish what they were.

I also practiced trying to place a key into a lock (Fig. 12). However, I lacked strength in my hand, so Erin taught me to tape the larger part of the house key to get some grip. Regardless, locking the key was impossible initially. We never think about day-to-day activities like unlocking and locking the front door. However, the act of holding the key with your fingers, pushing the key in the lock while rotating your wrist is actually very complex. Pushing in the key with the door closed did not work as I had no strength in my hand. However, I could turn the key with the door open if I held the door frame with my left hand. So, we added the key exercises to my repertoire. I opened the front door a few times each day and practiced it. I did not like the key exercise because it was hard, but I continued to try. I was determined that one day, I would open my house door with a key without relying on a keyless door lock.

I learned more domino exercises, placing them on their side and then upright, with the goal of not dropping them.

My thumb and index fingers were very swollen and weak. They were fine in the mornings, then gradually became swollen as the day went on. Erin suggested wrapping a finger compression cloth around them and using finger splinters with tape. This lasted for months and months, but I continued to wrap them in the afternoons, and the swelling would go down.

I wanted to tie my shoes. It was important for me to re-learn how to tie my shoes since the notion of buying shoes without laces appalled me. I was not interested in making my life easier; I wanted my life back, proper running shoes included! I think that helped me in the long run. Yes, it might have been easier to find workarounds, especially when my condition left me feeling exhausted. However, stimulating my brain, learning and re-learning new things, and getting my strength back was rewarding.

During one of our sessions, Erin gave me a practice shoe often used to teach children how to tie laces. Erin first had to show me how to do it since I could not remember. Where do you start? How to do it with only one hand? Yet another activity that we take for granted as soon as we learn how to do it! When I finally tried, I could not push the laces through the hole, as I had no strength in my right fingers. So, I did all the work with my left hand instead. My right fingers would try to push the lace through the hole, fail, then my left fingers would quickly pull and push the laces through. Dumitru bought me a new pair of large men's sneakers, put them on my working table, and I started practicing every day at home (Fig. 13-15). It took me weeks to push the laces through the holes and months to fully lace up the shoe until I could tie it on my own! By then, it was

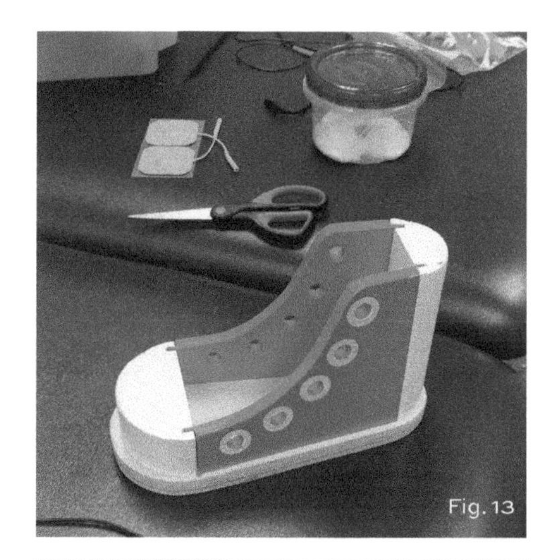
Fig. 13

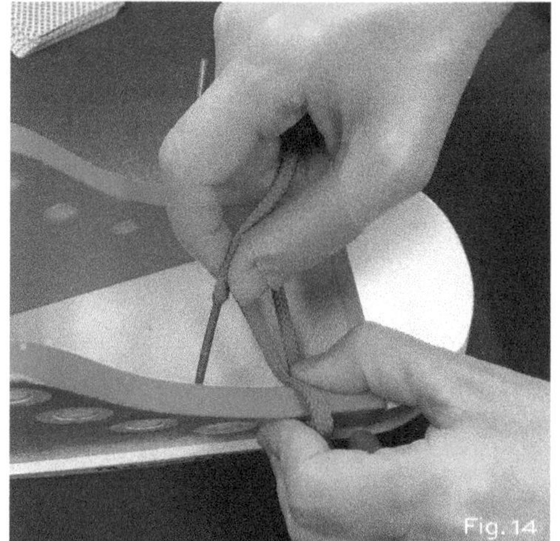
Fig. 14

Fig. 15

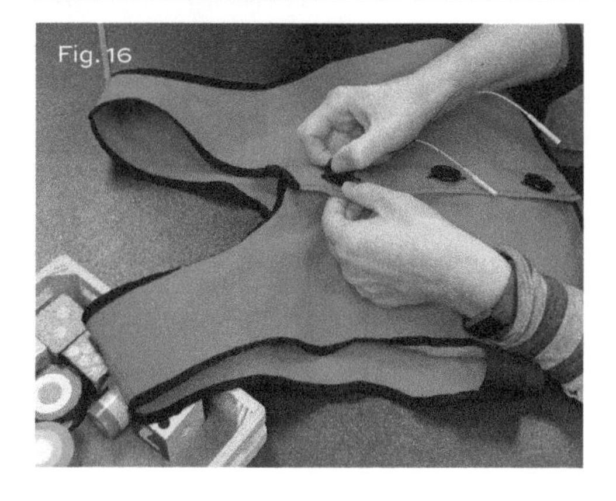
Fig. 16

already summer and sandal season, but I did not care; I would go out with my newly tied laces every day!

Erin also showed me techniques on how to button up my shirts. She told me to practice to gradually improve the dexterity of my right fingers rather than increasing the dexterity of my left hand. It was difficult. I could not close or open snap buttons at all—I did not have enough strength in my fingers (Fig. 16).

MARCH 28–31, 2019

Vacation

Dumitru and I went away for a few days at the end of March. This was our first trip after my artery dissection. I was nervous but excited too. I felt like I needed a vacation; I was tired of doctors and therapists.

APRIL 2019

10–12 Sessions in April

In early April, I started having breathing issues. First, I thought I had a minor cold, but the breathing issues got progressively worse in the following weeks. However, I continued with my sessions regardless.

I started using a physio band to exercise my thumb and index fingers. They go by colour, and yellow is the lightest one.

I also learned to trace a circle and follow it with my fingers. Then I learned how to trace my right hand with my left hand, then practiced spreading my fingers wide and closing them (Fig. 17).

I learned how to move my thumb and fingers while holding a small ball. I would look at how my left hand held the ball and mimic the movements with my right.

Erin suggested using suction cup balls. The goal was to throw the ball against a mirror to test the strength of my wrist. By now, I knew that it helped to try a few times with my left hand to get the feeling. Then I would try with my right. It was challenging at first, but after eight to ten times, I managed to throw the ball against the wall, and it did not fall! After the session with Erin, Dumitru ordered a pack of suction cup balls, and I started throwing them against the kitchen windows!

I continued using the finger compression cloth for my index finger during my naps and at night while I slept. This lasted for months until the swelling finally came down, and

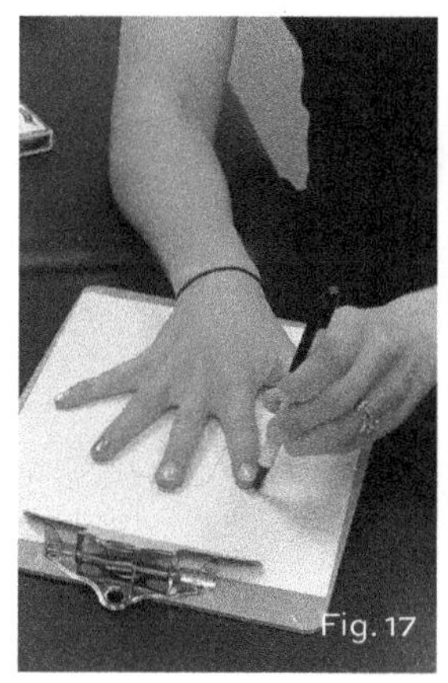
Fig. 17

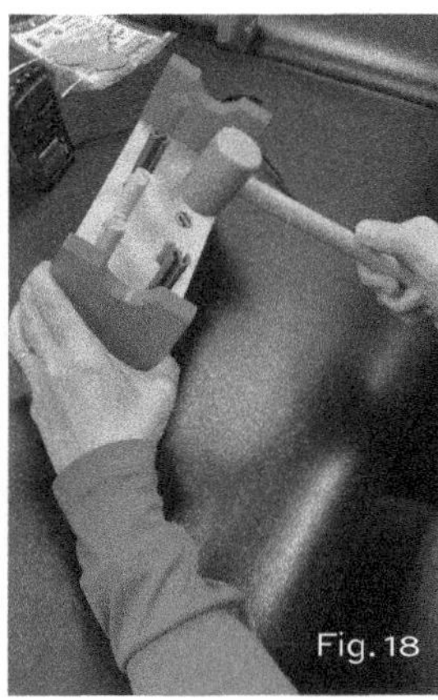
Fig. 18

Fig. 19

I could perform more fine motor tasks, such as holding a pen and working on writing properly again.

Erin suggested more exercises to put gentle pressure on my hand and fingers, such as using a plastic screwdriver and using a small wooden hammer to hit objects while holding my wrist in the correct position (Fig. 18), which was very hard at first. I would also use the hammer to practice rotating my wrist (Fig. 19). I learned how to make a small circle with my thumb and index fingers, making the "okay" sign.

MAY 2019

I continued to see Erin two to three times per week in May. I exercised daily, for 10–15 minutes at a time—two to three times in the morning and two to three times in the afternoon and evening.

Twisting and making small balls from the yellow putty was getting easier. I often practiced with the playing cards, trying to deal, shuffle, flip, and turn them.

I kept asking for exercises to stretch my arms as I felt I was getting very tight and stiff. By then, I was eager to get to a safe recovery gym. Before the artery dissection, I was very fit, with four to five gym sessions and a couple of short runs or tennis games per week. Now, I was moving very slowly, my joints ached, and I had a hard time going up and down a flight of stairs.

I started practicing opening and closing my thumb and each finger one at a time. It was tough as I had to go very slowly since my wrist and fingers would collapse easily. I learned how to use a gripper for finger strength. My fingers were very weak, but Erin told me not to focus too much on gripping hard. She told me to have patience, that my strength will come back with time, and that developing my fine motor skills was more important.

During the sessions with Erin, I would also practice using a yoga foam brick, holding it in different positions, and sometimes using the neuromuscular stimulation device (Fig. 20). Then I practiced using various books and magazines to get a better feel for their weight and width. I would sometimes walk with the books in my right hand for a few minutes at a time.

I then started using a small weight ball to hold and carry while ensuring that my fingers stayed closed and rounded over the ball for good wrist and finger positioning. I would

Fig. 20

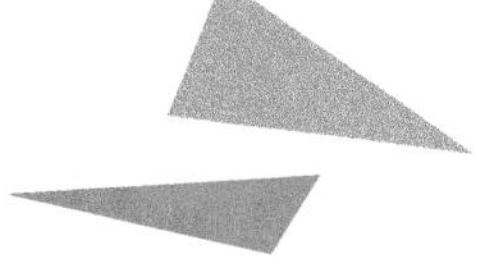

often check to see how my left hand held the ball and check if my right hand was doing the same.

I started to use therapy clothespins to practice the pincer grasp motion. Babies naturally develop this skill around nine months old. As adults, we do not remember how we learned this; we just know how to grasp things as needed. After a brain injury, one may need to re-learn this skill from scratch, while others lack the strength and coordination necessary to properly master things like holding a pen, manipulating small objects between their fingers, or buttoning up their blouse. Using clothespins and attaching them to a cup or a bowl is common in physiotherapy. I had to start with very small clothespins as I had almost no strength between my index finger and thumb.

Fig. 21

MAY 27, 2019

Colouring for the First Time

My first attempt at colouring did not go well (Fig. 21). I could not hold the crayon in my hand, so Erin suggested using a small ping pong ball held in my right palm. From then on, I practiced colouring daily—first for 5 minutes, then 10 minutes. At first, I felt uncomfortable having to practice colouring; I felt like a child. However, I did not show my embarrassment, knowing this was a means to an end after all.

I tried to write by hand, using a handbook from the Canadian Handwriting Series. This was difficult as I had completely lost the ability to spell in my native language (Romanian) and most of my ability to spell in English. Every attempt to write caused me to burst into tears as I realized I could not spell. So, I stuck to colouring for many months.

Erin taught me how to trace my right hand using my left hand with a crayon—first, with my fingers spread out, then closed. Then I tried to open and close my fingers on the paper to see how far I could spread them. It was a great daily exercise.

I then started to pick up small marbles with my fingers, one at a time, between my thumb and each finger in turn. I also learned to throw a small ball against the wall and catch it. I practiced doing this a lot, hoping to play tennis again in the future.

By late May, I started going to a gym twice a week. I felt weak, my joints hurt, and I got out of breath very quickly. I was keen to get permission from my doctors to exercise for 30 minutes twice per week. I started combining the activities from Erin with some exercises from the gym trainers. I was very fortunate to meet trainers specializing in brain recovery as it is essential not to overdo things. Despite the breathing challenges I was experiencing, I was happy to move a little. I continued to walk daily for 30–45 minutes, avoiding any hills.

JUNE 2019

In June, I only had six physiotherapy sessions. The breathing issues continued through the previous months, culminating with the discovery that I had developed a large intubation granuloma in my throat in early June. This sometimes happens in women who are intubated as they have a narrower windpipe, and it can cause lesions that may go unnoticed for a while. At least now I understood why I had difficulty breathing. The specialist confirmed that I had to see a surgeon in mid-June. The surgeon put me on prednisone for 12 days to avoid surgery. It was confirmed that it did not work by late June, and I needed day surgery to remove the granuloma. June was a difficult month. However, I looked forward to seeing Erin and seeing progress with my right arm and hand. In a way, this provided a nice distraction from the other medical stuff going on at the same time.

I learned how to open and close my right fist. I learned how to rotate my thumb across the tips of my fingers, across the middle of my joints, and the base of my fingers. This was very hard, as I could not reach that part at all. I added more exercises, including threading beads on a string and placing small plastic cylinders on a plastic board to create patterns. This was fun.

I continued to use putty to lengthen, stretch, and strengthen my fingers; tenting, opening, and closing my fingers; and hammering wooden pegs to strengthen my wrist using a wooden hammer. I also started using one-pound weights to strengthen my wrist (Fig. 22).

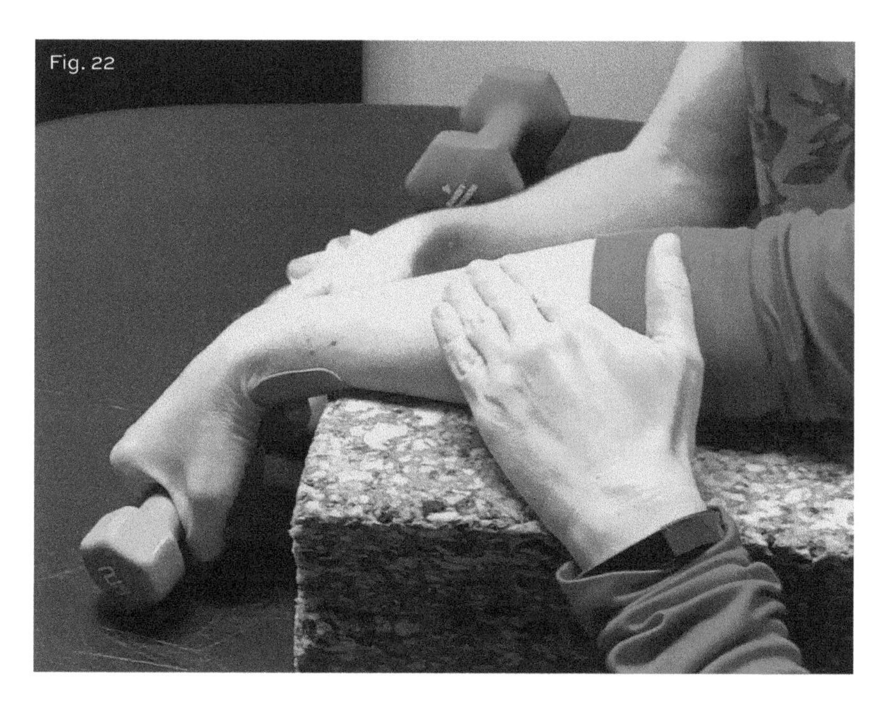
Fig. 22

I practiced rolling my index finger in and out, as it was still swollen daily. I kept my fingers vertical and tried to open and close them, using my left hand to spread the right. I would place my palm on the table, lifting one finger at a time. In the beginning, I could not lift my fingers at all, so I used my left hand to lift them. Eventually, my fingers started to move up a little. Within two days, I could see improvements in both exercises!

I learned how to bounce a ball and catch it. I tried this in various ways to see how it felt. I practiced bouncing the ball to Dumitru to get more feedback, which was challenging as the movement was unpredictable.

I also improved my ability to pull a plastic card between my right thumb and fingers as I tried to hold onto the plastic card, keeping it in my left hand.

I used TheraBand flexbars and would bend them up, down, and twist them. I bought a yellow and a red one, as one was easier and the other harder.

I continued to practice flipping over playing cards, as my wrist was still very weak. I needed to go slow and be very aware of my hand and wrist position.

JULY 2019

I had laryngology surgery in mid-July. I resumed my physiotherapy with weekly sessions.

Since my hand was recovering well, the therapist recommended using the neuromuscular stimulation device daily.

I learned three exercises that included two sets of twelve repetitions: webspace on the back of the hand—pinch the thumb and index; thumb muscle on the palmar aspect of hand—touch the pinky with the thumb; back of the hand

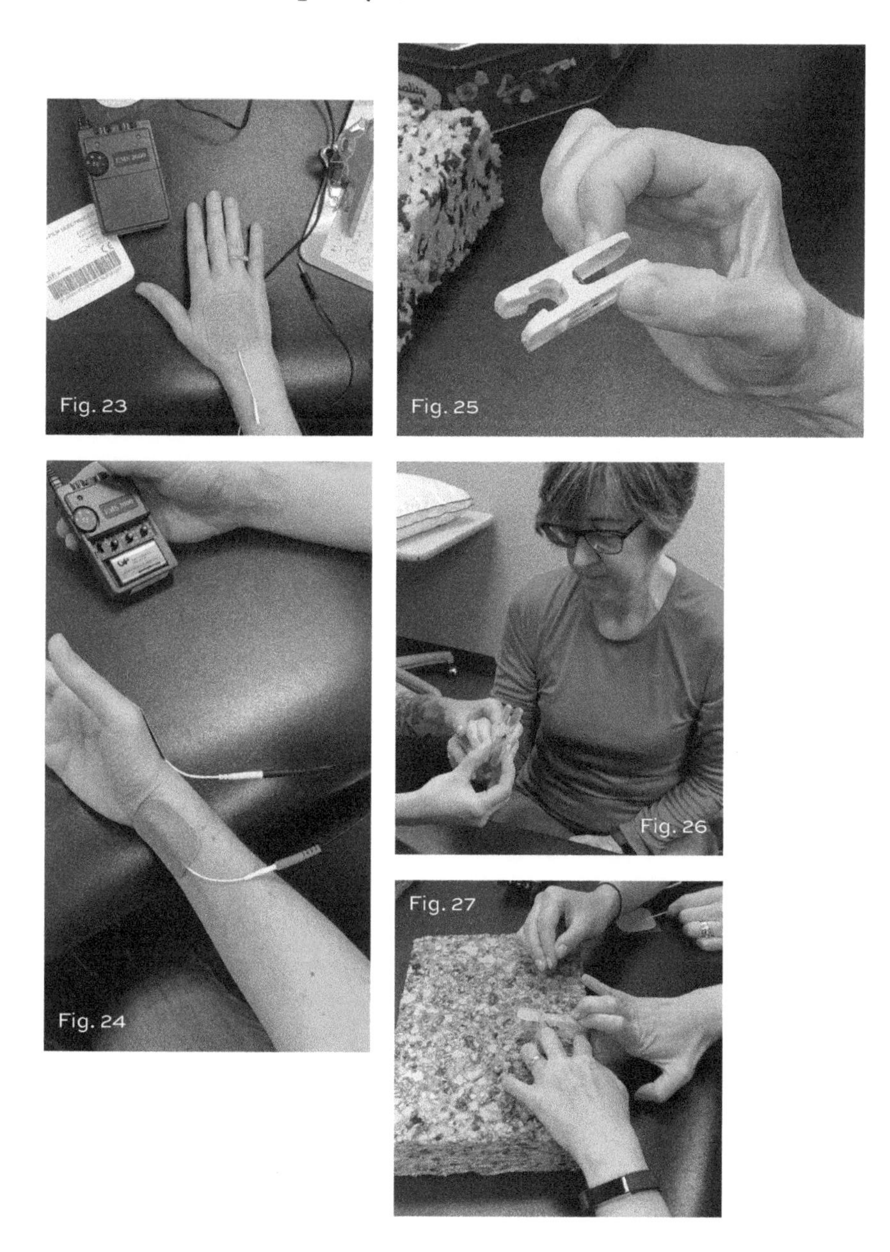
Fig. 23

Fig. 25

Fig. 24

Fig. 26

Fig. 27

below the knuckles and in line with the index finger and middle fingers—wave.

After that, I used the device for twenty minutes twice a day. The exercises were relatively simple, yet I needed time to do them right. I would have to pause for a minute between sets, then repeat.

I continued to use the yellow TheraBand by keeping the band in my left hand and pulling it with the right, trying to keep my fingers straight as I pulled. I would take a break between each finger.

In late July, I started to use a harder putty—medium red—to work more on pinching and elongating my fingers. I also continued playing with coins, trying to touch the coins with the tip of my index and slowly moving the coins from one finger to the next.

Using the neuromuscular stimulation device, I would slide my index finger on different surfaces. This would go on for months as my index finger was very weak (Fig. 23-24).

I started using different types of clothespins, rotating them in my hand in various positions. I would mimic what my left hand was doing with my right, making a circle with my index and thumb, like the letter C (Fig. 25-27).

AUGUST 2019

By August, I gradually reduced my physiotherapy sessions to every other week. I kept practicing my exercises while going to the gym twice a week (30 minutes) and walking daily (1 hour). I also started playing tennis again. At first, I would wrap a towel over the racket as my wrist was still very weak. This was strange, and I felt very self-conscious. I did not want people to see me like that. However, our tennis club community was very nice, and everyone was incredibly supportive. I was determined to play properly again.

In the beginning, I would just learn to hold the tennis racket, and then I would throw the ball gently with my left hand and try to hit it with my right. Dumitru helped me hit the ball from a meter away from the net. The ball would hit the net most of the time. I would only play for 5 minutes; then I would rest, lasting about 30 minutes at a time. However, I could see improvements very quickly, so I continued to try. We played two to three times per week as the weather was nice. Every week, I could hit a bit longer. By the end of the month, I could consistently hit the ball

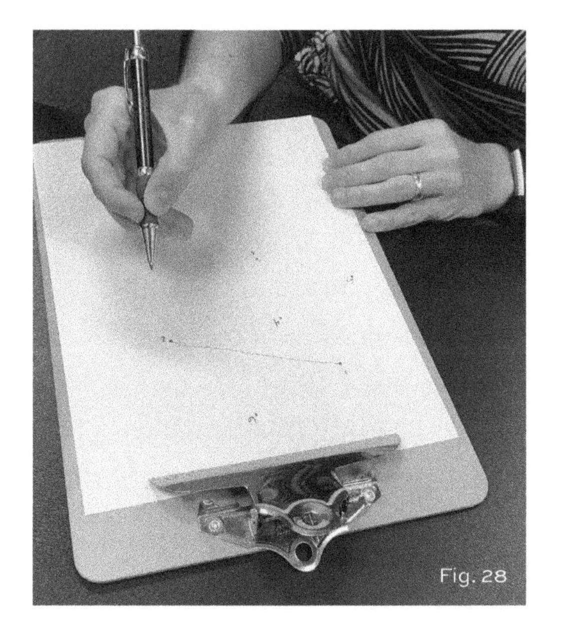

Fig. 28

over the net from about 2 meters away, so I started to back up a bit more. I was always right-handed but had a powerful double-handed backhand. My forehand was always a weaker shot for me, so I was not surprised that I had to work on it from scratch.

Erin then taught me how to trace on paper by making dots first, then connecting the dots, and keeping the line as straight as possible (Fig. 28). By now, I was starting to enjoy exercises that required colouring! I realized I did not like colouring in geometric patterns, as I found it boring. So, I purchased an adult colouring book that appealed to me—flowers, castles, gardens, and small animals. After that, I enjoyed colouring and would spend 15–20 minutes on it most days.

We also focused on more tenting work with yellow putty using my left hand to push down on my right index finger gently. Erin would also have me bury marbles in the putty, and then I would have to get them out with my right hand. She would then get me to drop the marbles into a cup, one at a time.

I also learned to hold small items and slowly rotate my wrist up, down, left, and right without dropping the objects.

I would use the red putty to create small rings and then spread them with my fingers to stretch them.

Using a light wrist weight band (0.5 lb.), Erin would have me lift my fingers while keeping my arm straight on one or two foam bricks, focusing on my wrist strength.

SEPTEMBER 2019

In September, I had two sessions with Erin, which included more exercises with bouncy balls, catching the balls in different directions, and using the balls to get more control over my right thumb. The exercises were now more repetitive, with fewer new changes and more focus on specific exercises that were still difficult. I gradually spent less time on hand therapy and more time on things I used to like.

I always enjoyed gardening but did not have much time for it. We started going out to the garden for 15–20 minutes every day for fresh air back in March. However, the garden was in terrible shape—the hydrangeas were not cut, and we had neglected the leaves and branches blown by the wind for two months. I remember teaching Dumitru how to cut the hydrangeas properly. Over the following months, I was able to do a few things by myself as Dumitru watched closely to ensure I was not overdoing it. This helped, and I still remember the little victories—our friends helped Dumitru set up the tomato seeds we had grown indoors for years, and I guided Dumitru as the seedlings started to sprout and needed to be replanted. The seedlings had grown tall in late June, and we needed to keep them upright. I tried—unsuccessfully at first—to use garden Velcro ties. In August, I started pinching delicate flowers (bacopas, petunias), which was great practice for my right fingers as I used the pincer grasp on petals and small leaves.

In early September, I started taking care of our greenhouse—staking tomatoes and using garden scissors to prune them. It took Dumitru and me a few months to realize that scissors were indeed designed to be used for either left or right-handed people! Same for pruners! For a Romanian brought up in a communist dictatorship, I always assumed that everyone used their right hand for most tasks. Of course, I knew there are left-handed tennis players, left-handed writers, etc. However, my experience was coloured by my perception. As a child growing up in the mid-1970s in Romania, we could not use our left hand for writing or playing sports. My older sister was left-handed, and she was strongly discouraged from using her left hand. Because of this, she believes she was left with two bad hands—not good at anything requiring fine motor skills and hand-eye coordination. I was a very compliant child, so I do not ever remember trying to use my left hand because, in my mind, it was simply not allowed. Coming to Canada, we did not have children or teenagers around, so we were quite oblivious to so many tools that could have been helpful for people who suffered a brain injury or an accident. I found it interesting that none of the therapists I had seen for about seven months mentioned it!

I have mixed feelings about this. On the one hand, this may have made my life easier in the first months since opening an envelope by hand or using the right-handed paper knife or scissors is frustrating and can be dangerous when you are on blood thinners. On the other hand, this motivated me to work hard on my recovery, so I continued using tiny right-handed scissors and pruners for almost a year before using normal-sized tools again. Being aware of using left-handed tools (scissors, pruners) may have helped me at first. However, this may also have encouraged me to stop using my right hand, which would not have helped in the long run.

On September 15, 2019, I attended the annual Terry Fox Run. Dumitru and I had participated in the 5 km or 10 km run for years. We received the run registration in August. I was walking for 45 minutes per day at a slow pace by that time, so the thought of walking the course seemed doable. With support from a couple of friends, we walked the 5 km distance in over an hour at a slow pace. Dumitru ran the 10 km and then came back to join us as we finished. I felt so proud of myself.

OCTOBER 2019

I did not have physiotherapy this month. However, I continued going to the gym twice a week and walking daily, with the odd tennis rally when the weather was nice. I also continued to exercise daily for 30 minutes. Nonetheless, I noticed I had gradually reverted to using my left hand more than my right with fewer therapy sessions. When I went to physiotherapy two to three times per week, Erin had always reminded me to use my right hand, correct position, etc. This was a concern, yet I was dealing with other areas of my recovery at the same time.

NOVEMBER 2019

In November, I saw Erin once. We focused on exercising my fingers using three-pound weights, spreading my fingers over the ball, and walking with it. She would also get me to use the same ball to push my right index finger to the left, then right.

I bought a spiky ball (about the size of a Pilates ball) and started tossing the ball up and catching it in my palm. It was easy to do with my left hand but challenging with my right.

Erin also had me hold an elastic over my fist and try to spread my fingers with control. We tried various elastic exercises to strengthen my index finger (up, down, left, right, push, pull). We went back to the rice box exercises to test my progress, and I showed much improvement!

A couple of years prior, I had participated in a cookie exchange with a small group of friends. I was never good at baking but wanted to do more outside of work, so I joined when they invited me in 2017. I was stressed, thinking my baking would not be good enough. However, I got away with it for two years by making no-bake treats. I enjoyed the get-togethers; the ladies were funny, kind, and witty.

After my brain injury, my friends sent me well wishes and stayed in touch as I started my recovery. They knew I had just come out of the hospital when I was supposed to celebrate my 50th birthday. So, they organized a birthday celebration for me. I could not use my right hand at that time, but they were thoughtful, and I felt I could enjoy the meal and company without feeling too self-conscious.

Fast forward to September 2019, I received an email inviting me to the cookie exchange—being invited after my brain injury came as a big surprise. I did not think I could bake cookies this year! Dumitru talked to me about it and asked, "Why not?" I did not want to inconvenience him as he was already busy with work and driving me back and forth to therapy sessions three to four times per week.

However, he loves a particular type of Romanian mini croissant, so he suggested I try baking some with his help. He also reminded me that I would have many opportunities for hand therapy as I had to cut the dough into squares, place the filling, and roll each square to form the mini-croissants.

We had a blast for the next couple of months; it took three attempts for the result to be tasty and look good, but the feedback from my friends was positive. In addition, I decided to print black and white Christmas cards and colour them by hand, which was relaxing and enjoyable.

After many months of therapy, we went away for a week from late November to early December. I was happy to be away for a while, looking forward to a change in scenery and routine.

DECEMBER 2019

Dumitru and all my Romanian friends ski every winter. I would go with them, but I did not enjoy it. I liked the scenery, especially on warm sunny days, but I was always afraid of falling. I was prudent and did okay on most blue runs, and I only went on the black runs if I had no other options.

A few years back, I took a tumble in bad weather and ended up in a pile of snow with my skis crossed. I hurt both my knees, but I was too embarrassed to ask for help and skied back, turning slowly and carefully. After that, I needed physiotherapy for almost a year, having suffered a grade-two tear of my MCL on both knees.

In December 2018, I decided to take adult ski lessons for three days, and I was excited about skiing in 2019! We went cross-country skiing in early February 2019, which was great, but then my brain injury happened.

So, I knew skiing was out of the question this year, and my mind was adjusting to the idea that I may not ski again as it was too risky. However, Dumitru would ski in the mornings, so I would practice my hand exercises while he was out.

While still away on our vacation in early December, I signed up for a conference call with a local brain injury or stroke survivor group that identified itself as "young." I was very interested in meeting with them as I had found that all the brain injury or stroke survivors I had come across to date were either not working or were already retired. At this time, I was still off work on long-term disability and dealing with a lot of therapy, but I was very keen to connect with other people who had gone back to work or were interested in going back. I wanted to learn from their experience and was curious about the activities they engaged in, the things that helped them, and the challenges and successes they were having.

The session was helpful, although unexpected. I had contacted the group coordinator by email, as I needed to explain that I had a hard time with groups. I had tried a speech therapy group in May 2019. At that time, I knew I had completely lost my ability to spell, but my spoken English was fine. My first language, Romanian, was quite affected; I could not speak Romanian well at all. The Romanian language requires that adjectives agree with nouns or pronouns, so it's easy to notice a foreigner even if they speak perfect Romanian. Within days after my surgery, I had a hard time speaking Romanian. Dumitru and I had spoken Romanian all the time, switching to English only when talking about IT and management terms.

Immediately after my injury, I spoke very little as I was too tired most of the time. The doctors did not realize anything was wrong as I responded in English; although they knew I did not speak much, they expected that. I learned about aphasia much later. Aphasia is a condition that affects one's ability to communicate. It usually occurs after a brain injury, stroke, or head injury. This condition can affect one's ability to speak, write, and understand language. Those affected can speak fine, like in my case, but can lose their ability to spell. Some people must re-learn their own language from scratch. Other people cannot read at all or have difficulty reading after the brain injury. Some people recover their ability to communicate within days or weeks, others within months or years, and some people never recover. So, when I attended the first and last speech therapy session in May 2019, I was confronted with writing, reading, and paraphrasing my answers in front of four other people. I did not know until October 2019 that I had an issue with reading. I was right-handed, and my right arm and hand were paralyzed. I could not hold a pen, and I was asked to do my best to write using my left hand. In that session in May 2019, all I knew was that I was exposed; everyone could see that I could not hold a pen and could not spell. I was overwhelmed by talking in front of everyone, and I started to cry. The other participants and the therapist were very kind, but I did not feel comfortable trying again. I thought I had upset the other patients and made it hard for the therapist to do her job, so I stopped attending the group. I tried speech therapy again in October 2019, but it did not go well. I was quite nervous about any group interaction after that.

Back to the conference call, the coordinator understood and told me I could just listen without speaking. The session turned out to be a support group, with a counsellor facilitating the session. By August 2019, I had met a counsellor as I had an increasingly hard time talking to people. The counsellor helped me realize that I had developed post-traumatic stress disorder (PTSD) after the stent surgery. I knew I was not ready to participate in group counselling. However, one of the participants on that conference call shared her experience with GRASP, an innovative hand and arm therapy program that had helped her, and she encouraged everyone to try it.

As soon as I got home, I emailed the GRASP program. Between my continued struggle to spell and the not-so-user-friendly email address the GRASP program used, I eventually sent them my request for information on the program. By mid-December, I had a call from the program coordinator. Before Christmas, I had an in-person meeting with the organizers, and I was accepted into the program, starting in January 2020 for eight weeks.

GRASP

GRASP stands for Graded Repetitive Arm Supplementary Program. The program's name is a handful for someone who has suffered a stroke or a brain injury—the acronym is much easier to remember and say. I benefited from the program from January to February 2020 and June to August 2020. From what I understand, the program was created by the Department of Physical Therapy at the University of British Colombia and the GF Strong Rehabilitation Centre. In the following few pages, I will describe my experience with the program. My intention is to recall how it felt to go through the program over eight months. The program is based on easy-to-find and inexpensive equipment, a time commitment of one hour a day, and the willingness to take a leap of faith and trust the program. Thousands of challenging repetitions are needed for the brain to repair and rebuild new neuropathways required for recovery. The program also encourages participants to have family or friends help with the exercises, not only for physical support but also for motivation and moral support. Completing the exercises every day, seven days a week for eight to ten weeks, is much easier if you have a cheerleader!

When I was accepted into the program, I was apprehensive. After ten months of therapy, my arm was almost recovered, and my hand and wrist were a lot better. However, my fine motor skills were far from what I considered recovered; I could still barely hold a pen, my fingers had almost no strength, and my wrist was weak. I was also a bit tired of therapy. Toward the end of 2019, I had maxed out all my available extended health benefits and was mentally drained. I had overcome many challenges; the greatest difficulty was finding the way forward without a clear path to navigate our healthcare system. I felt like a detective on a constant chase, finding options through sheer luck or trial and error. While I was excited about starting GRASP, I was also nervous about meeting the other participants and therapists. My fear of feeling put on the spot, judged, and asked to speak in front of others was overwhelming. However, I wanted my hand and arm to recover fully, and I wanted to do everything that I could do before my brain injury. Call it perseverance or stubbornness, but I was driven to see results, especially as I continued to see improvements every week.

JANUARY–FEBRUARY 2020

We arrived at the Templeton Park Recreation Centre in Vancouver, BC, on Wednesday in early January 2020. The group was small, and the therapists immediately put us at ease. It was great to have Dumitru with me as I had a hard time following sometimes; I was still nervous and could not process the information and instructions quickly. Each participant was encouraged to talk a bit about their specific goals. We were given the GRASP manual. Physical hand and arm measurements were taken as a baseline to track our progress. Then we dived into a set of stretching exercises and a few of the first exercises. We were then told that every week, we would need to return to our group setting for one and a half hour sessions to talk about our progress, discuss any exercises that were too difficult or too easy, and have an opportunity to chat with the other participants or other family members. After the first session with the group, I was ecstatic and felt eager and excited about therapy again!

The next day came, and reality hit with a thud! I did not think about this before. Looking closer at my new manual, I realized that I had difficulty from the first exercise. Until then, I always had a therapist show me what to do, and sometimes I had to be shown a few times. The manual showed each exercise on one page, with pictures and a few steps to follow. I could read most words, but putting the words together in a sentence took a while. There were 35 exercises, and I only had one hour to complete them!

I was lost. Dumitru had to work, and I already had a hard time asking for help when it came to reading issues. However, I stuck with the exercises every day, even though I needed closer to three hours to finish at first. By the end of the week, I had completed the exercises in two hours. As the next weeks rolled by, I had completed the exercises in 90 minutes.

Being used to gym exercises and having good body awareness, I took my time and did not allow myself to rush through. I was always very flexible, so stretching felt good for the warm-up section, and I stretched, especially when I did the finger exercises. Being naturally built with hypermobility in my fingers meant that I had to be careful not to push too hard or rush through, and I found that the stretching breaks allowed me to get better results on the putty exercises.

My private hand physiotherapy prepared me for the exercises as I had most of the equipment available, including weights (Fig. 29-33). In the beginning, I used 0.5-pound weights for most of the shoulder, elbow, and wrist exercises. Three to four weeks later, I moved up to 1-pound, then 2-pound weights. The manual offered options for suggested sets and repetitions. Again, I learned from the therapists to be patient and not go too fast too soon.

The coordination exercises were relatively easy for me to complete; however, I could not do them fast partly because my dominant hand was slow and partly because I was stressed when rushed—the line between pushing myself and feeling rushed to feeling overwhelmed and anxious was very thin. I wanted to play tennis again, so I was keen to try the tennis ball exercises. Rolling the ball and dropping and catching the ball exercises were faster in a few weeks, and by the end of the first program, I started juggling with two balls.

I had never had the time to iron clothes. I often paired my business suits with iron-free shirts. My hand therapist suggested ironing tea towels in late summer, with a low setting and a small iron. I practiced once a week for 15–20 minutes. Something about ironing out the wrinkles and putting pressure on my hand in the process felt good. I then added one of Dumitru's shirts to my recovery repertoire. By the time I was doing the GRASP program, the folding laundry exercises were easy for me, as was buttoning my shirts until I realized that women's and men's shirts are different. Most women's shirts have the button on the left side, and

Fig. 29

Fig. 30

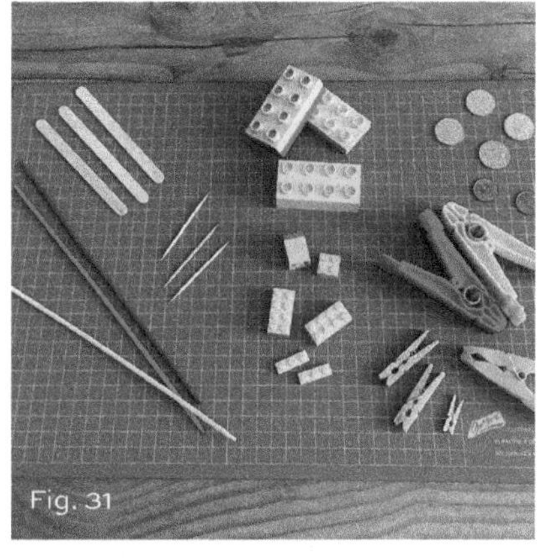

Fig. 31

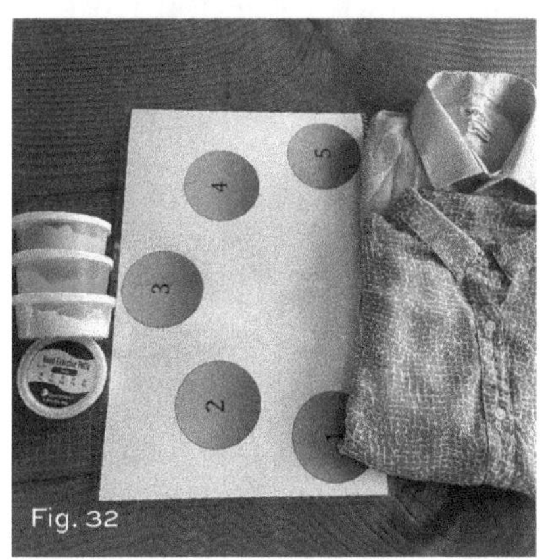

Fig. 32

Fig. 33

most men's shirts have the buttons on the right side. I never thought about it, and I do not think the GRASP therapists did either. However, I practiced buttoning both ladies' and men's shirts, so I doubled the exercises and quickly became fast and accurate (provided the material was not too stiff as my strength was not there yet).

The exercises with blocks and Lego pieces were interesting. At first, I could not use the Lego pieces I had; they were okay in size, but they were very stiff. Dumitru would have to take them apart if I managed to push them in as I could not un-stack them. So, we went to the dollar store and bought a set made from softer plastic, which made a big difference. I learned that I needed to find a balance and not push myself so hard that I would get discouraged or hurt myself in the process.

Once I got the hang of the exercises from the GRASP manual, I started to play with different types of sticks (from popsicle sticks to real pickup sticks to toothpicks), large and small paper clips, and different sizes of coins. The paper clips were more of a brain challenge than a fine motor skill challenge (like the reading issues I had, I needed time to figure out how to string the paper clips and push them on and off). The coins were interesting too. Most of us rarely deal with cash, let alone coins, and I had not owned a piggy bank since elementary school! So, flipping coins seemed a bit useless. However, the movement of flipping items was useful, so I would flip coins and my Lego pieces and turn them on their side in various positions to make it more interesting.

Using the GRASP progress tracker was instrumental. Seeing results every day and every week made it real, and it motivated me. Trusting the process was necessary. Sometimes, I did not see results for days; sometimes, I did not see any results for weeks (my finger strength exercises were so slow). There were 35 exercises in the program, but I could see minor improvements every day, on other exercises, and after a while, it became easier to be patient. We were not required to complete the thousands of repetitions every day. However, I was doing a few hundred repetitions without even realizing it daily. This had amounted to a few thousand repetitions within the first eight weeks, and the progress was clear!

The GRASP program is built to allow participants an opportunity to check on their progress every week to assess how well they did in the previous week. The subjective assessment is a good personal gauge. Being a perfectionist, I was disappointed in Week 1 as I had only used my right hand about 65% of the time. However, by Week 8, I could see improvement and saw I was using my right hand almost 90% of the time!

One of the most useful aspects of the program is the list of activities that the participant wants to commit to at the beginning. The list is customized to one's interests, needs, and goals. My list was short at first because I was learning to write again at the same time. Then I kept adding items. I also learned a lot from the other participants and the therapists, as each session allowed us to brainstorm ideas and hear what others had tried.

Below is my final list after the first program:

- Put the dishes away one by one with my right hand
- Turn the light switches on and off with my right index
- Play piano (by that, I mean learn how to play as I had never played the piano before)
- Fold the laundry and iron weekly
- Floss and brush my teeth with my right hand
- Dice and stir my food when cooking with my right hand
- Wear a hair elastic around my right wrist as a reminder to use my right hand as much as possible
- Eat with my right hand
- Brush and blow-dry my hair with my right hand
- Curl my hair with my right hand

I also tried cross-country skiing. As I had cross-country skied before, I was surprised to realize that my balance was better than ever! I stayed on flat trails and only used classic skis (skate skiing was challenging for me before; I had tried without much success), and the poles gave me good exercise for my arms. I enjoyed being outdoors, in the sun or fresh snow, so I cross-country skied almost every week during the program!

At the end of the first program, we met at the recovery site to see the results. I was pleased with the result but started to get nervous about the next step. As it was near the end of February, we started to hear things about COVID-19, so we were grateful to have finished the initial program.

MARCH–MAY 2020

I continued the exercises in March, with three to four days of exercises per week. At that time, most therapists abruptly stopped working as the health care system—including everyone else in the world—was trying to make sense of what was happening. As we learned more about COVID-19, my anxiety started to build again. After excellent progress on my hand and arm, I was concerned about receiving physiotherapy amid the pandemic. Fortunately, by late March, many recovery programs resumed online. It was remarkable considering that the organizers had to quickly figure out how to provide programs to address a wide range of participants' needs.

Some sessions were a bit rocky at the beginning. I can recall that I was distressed when, in the first Zoom session, the coordinator quickly explained the agenda and immediately started a round of brain games involving reading, writing, and spelling. I expected a hand therapy session, not group communication and speech therapy! I am a technology manager and am very good at applications, software, etc. However, since I felt I would be in the spotlight, I panicked and froze. I did not think I could simply say, "I don't want to read or write or spell something." So, after a second or two, I just slammed my MacBook shut. I needed twenty minutes to collect myself before providing feedback to the organizers and trying virtual therapy again.

The challenge with one's dominant hand after a stroke is that since it is still much weaker than one's other hand, it becomes second nature to use the non-dominant one. Without realizing it, one's body simply forgets about the dominant hand and relies on the other to do day-to-day activities. Back in December 2019, I had caught a glimpse of myself in the mirror and realized I looked like an invalid—my right shoulder was slumped, my right arm and hand hung by my body, and my left hand was doing what I needed to get ready in the morning: floss and brush my teeth, shower, comb my hair, and so on. By the end of March 2020, I noticed I had regressed from the end of February 2020. The progress from the eight weeks of the GRASP program was gradually going away. The distraction of the pandemic did not help either.

I was pleased to receive an email about the next GRASP program in mid-May, offered virtually. I knew first-time participants would get priority, so I was not guaranteed a spot in the program. I waited eagerly and was delighted when I learned that I was accepted into the virtual program, this time for a ten-week session.

JUNE–AUGUST 2020

When I started the second GRASP program, I decided to limit the exercises to one hour per day. I was now familiar with the exercises and knew the key to success was the regularity and quality of the daily exercises. As a perfectionist, I was tempted to exercise more, but I capped my workouts at one hour, which gave me more time to do other things I enjoyed.

Instead of increasing the number of repetitions, I increased the weights. By the end of the second program, I had graduated from 0.5-pound to 8-pound weights. When the pandemic started, it was difficult to find dumbbells. I already had 2-pound and 3-pound weights and a set of 5-pound dumbbells, so I used those for my GRASP activities. It took me two months to find 8-pound weights, but I used those for the rest of the program once I did.

Staying aware of my body was very important. It was easier to correct myself once I realized that my body would default to using my non-dominant hand.

Although I made efforts to use my right hand, it took five weeks of the second program to make my right hand my dominant hand again. I was thrilled when I went to take out a dish from the oven one day and reached with my right-hand oven glove without thinking about it!

Later, I added more to my list of activities in the second GRASP program.

Knitting is great for recovery as it provides repetition, focus, and it can be fun! I had a blast with a group of girlfriends who helped me start a knitting project at the end of the first GRASP program. I had learned to knit in Grade 2 or 3 as a mandatory school activity. However, I did not remember how to cast on, and I realized that my girlfriends were all knitting differently. I followed their instructions and could start a very simple scarf purl pattern, but the knitting action and the needles' position felt very strange. I had to pause and rest my hands for a while. After about fifteen minutes, I picked up my knitting and, without even thinking, my hands started knitting with ease. My friends looked at me with interest but said nothing. Months later, I realized that I had been taught continental knitting instead of British, Canadian/American knitting! The movement of the hands and fingers is different between the two styles. During the second GRASP program, I continued my knitting project and was proud to show my progress at the weekly virtual sessions.

I also continued to colour, draw, play tennis, garden, play the piano, and play with hairdos and makeup. Any activity I engaged in benefitted my recovery.

At the beginning of my recovery, I started putting dishes away one at a time, trying to use my right hand. Then I would quickly do the job with my left hand. In time, I picked up two dessert plates instead of one. Then I picked up two appetizer plates, eventually picking up two main course plates with my right hand.

One day, I tried using my right hand to hold an umbrella. I could only do it for a few seconds, but I would try again several minutes later. Within weeks, I noticed that my right hand and arm were stronger.

During my lengthy walks, I started carrying a mug and practiced switching the mug from my left to my right hand. With every step of the way, I would watch my wrist and correct my position. After several months of making a point of always trying to hold my cup with my right hand, I no longer had to think about it!

I believe the key to my success was challenging myself slowly and safely, trying new things to stimulate my brain, and improving my fine motor skills.

At the end of the second GRASP program, I was confident that my physical recovery was almost complete. I remained aware of my body and challenged myself; I did not become complacent. I continued online gym courses two to three times per week, staying aware of my posture and building up my strength. After seven half-marathons, I knew I would never run again. However, I look forward to walking charity races when the pandemic is over. We are designed to move our bodies, and our brains crave stimulation and repetition; we just need to find what motivates us and keep striving to improve and have fun!

EMOTIONAL RECOVERY

As I continued to work on my physical recovery, I struggled with my emotional state. While I was very focused on my physical recovery, I kept trying to find a path toward brain recovery. Six months after the stent surgery, I still did not know why I had such a hard time reading; I could not write well, and re-learning to spell took time. I felt some health practitioners had written me off. "Don't worry about spelling; no one can spell these days." This was of little help for a knowledge worker like me, whose job is to think for a living!

By early summer of 2019, I had given up on the idea that speech therapists could help me, and I was increasingly worried about returning to work. By late summer of 2019, my family doctor recognized that I needed to see someone to help me with post-traumatic stress disorder (PTSD). This is not uncommon in people that recover from major surgery. As I started on the long emotional recovery journey, I came across a speech-language pathologist therapist who was assessing my voice, and she realized that I could not read properly. It all made sense; the trauma, the inability to read aloud, and the inability to speak up, literally and metaphorically. It would take me almost two years to understand, document, and be able to share the following chapters.

POST-TRAUMATIC STRESS DISORDER

I had lived in fear all my life. It was who I was; I don't ever remember being different. From early recollections of my childhood (around two years old), I remember being at my grandparents' house and playing in a corner alone with my older brothers and grandparents. If I heard a knock on the door, even before the steps got closer, my heart would beat faster, my throat would tighten, and I would not relax until whoever was at the door left. I do not recall any specific event that would have caused such trauma apart from two distant memories. A few times, my brothers and cousins would chase me around the house with a feather, pretending it was an insect, and one time a distant female cousin, who was younger but much larger than me, chased me in an attempt to hug me. I was not yet three years old at the time. My family always recounts how funny it was for them to see me running away and crying as she tried to catch me and hug me. I still remember the fear of being chased and the embarrassment since I was older and should not have been afraid of her.

I grew up in Romania during the communist dictatorship (1947–1989). I come from a mixed family—my mom was born in Romania from a Hungarian ethnicity, and my father's family was Romanian. So, I grew up in a Hungarian Catholic and a Romanian Christian Orthodox family when the regime pushed for atheism and discouraged religion. My mother's family (Hungarian) had a deep distrust of most Romanians, especially the communist regime, while the communist regime persecuted my father's side (Romanian). My paternal grandfather was a Christian Orthodox priest. He died relatively young, soon after the communist regime came to power. I never knew the details as we, the children, never talked about it in our family. Everyone quickly silenced the rare hushed conversations I would overhear. My grandfather may have died of a heart attack as the communist acolytes confiscated the last piece of land that was theirs. Two of my father's older brothers who tried to protect their father were thrown in jail, one of them serving ten years. After he graduated from his teaching program, my father was sent to mandatory military service for three years (which was much more than the standard military service). This three-year mandatory military service was reserved for young soldiers from an "unhealthy origin."

I heard that term many times growing up. I heard it on TV, read it in books, and heard it in school. A person with a "healthy origin" was typically brought up in a family of workers or a family of small farmers that rented rather than owned land. On the other hand, a person with an "unhealthy origin" was brought up in a family that owned land or had a profession, such as teachers, priests, doctors, judges, etc. In the early 1950s, a person from an "unhealthy origin" was often persecuted in some shape or form. When

I was in school in the 1980s, I knew I would not be allowed to study certain subjects such as history, economics, law, psychology, sociology, medicine, etc. It was just something I knew and had to accept. It was also something one did not talk about outside of the immediate family, as it was not safe.

The two families did not get together often. They lived about 350 km away from one another. My father and mother would drop us off for summer vacation when we were young. My father spent a few hours in between trains. He made polite conversation with my maternal grandfather and smiled politely at my maternal grandmother (she did not speak Romanian). My mother spent a few days with us after the drop-off but would leave shortly after as she also had to go back to work. As soon as we were alone, my grandfather forbade us from speaking Romanian; we were to speak Hungarian as we had quickly forgotten it. We were all compliant, especially me, so I never complained; I just found it difficult, and I felt embarrassed because I did not speak the language well. I was always quiet, but I was even more so during this time. I would make excuses not to engage in conversation and attend to my summer reading for school instead.

My first language was Hungarian. I spent a couple of years in a Hungarian village before moving to the town in which my father worked. In the second grade, I told my peers about my summer vacation and talked to them about my Hungarian family and speaking Hungarian. I learned very quickly that this was a mistake—the sting from their judgements around those who spoke another language aside from Romanian was and is still present. I never told anyone from school about my Hungarian family again.

I started pre-school when I was three, and all my schooling was in Romanian. By the time I went to pre-school, I knew I could not talk to anyone about my family. This was in the '70s, and the communist regime system relied on an extensive network of informants. It was critical that children from an "unhealthy origin" did not disclose any information that could put them and their families at risk. I do not recall being told not to talk to my peers, teachers, or others about my family; it had to have been subtler than that, but I am unsure. I just know that I lived with a constant fear inside me—the fear that I may be thrown out of school, that my parents may be thrown in jail, or that I had done something wrong. My parents and close relatives constantly told us that we had to get good grades and attend a good university, as we could not rely on anyone else to help us get through life.

As I grew up, I carried this fear with me in school and university. I was twenty when the communist regime was overthrown. I graduated with a degree in mathematics and started working for a large management consulting firm. I came to Canada when I was thirty and continued to work for several large firms. Although I had a successful career and was comfortably settled in Canada, the fear never left me; it was always there in the background, not visible to most people. I realized I was increasingly becoming stressed, but I just ignored it. Dealing with stress was just a part of life, or so I thought. After all, I was happy at home, enjoyed my work, and was healthy. I exercised, ran, and played tennis, and I enjoyed my time with friends. I had headaches and migraines often, but I accepted this fact as a part of my life.

On that fateful morning of February 7, 2019, when I woke up in the hospital after experiencing a migraine, I was disorientated. The following two days were a blur, and then everything went dark as I collapsed. I woke up after a while, at night, and I had a strange sense that something was very wrong. I was aware it was dark as I lay in a bed. I could not see much without my eyeglasses, so I saw shadows gliding around the floor, moving around the bed. I suddenly felt terrified, and the fear surrounded and drowned me, rising from my gut to my throat. I did not know who I was, where I was, or what had happened. I was frightened to my core, shaking, and unable to scream or move. A shadow got closer to the bed. I remember saying, "Please, make it stop," but I was unaware of any pain. The shadow moved closer, and then I did not remember anything. The following day, I woke up in the hospital bed with the sun coming through the window. Dumitru was there, and he gently put my eyeglasses on and greeted me. I did not say anything about the previous night; I thought I had had a bad dream. He did not tell me anything about the stent surgery; I only learned about it weeks later.

I woke up several times with the same sense of fear. I was still in the hospital and was taken from my room for a scan. I fell asleep on the gurney and woke up suddenly.

It was dark again, and I did not have my eyeglasses, but I could see the shadows moving around me. The fear was back. At first, I did not hear anything, but then I saw lights and heard steps coming toward me. I wanted to scream, I wanted to run, but I could not move. I said again, "Please, make it stop." I must have either fallen asleep or been given a pill, as I would wake up back in my hospital room. I still did not mention anything to Dumitru.

It took weeks for me to learn the details about what happened. I either did not remember or did not process the information. We were going for a walk when Dumitru told me about the decisions he had to make and the lengthy wait as the stents were put in. He made light of it and emphasized how lucky I was to be alive. We did not talk too much about it as I got tired quickly, and we were both dealing with my therapy sessions almost daily for weeks.

About two months after being released from the hospital, I had my first flashback as we walked on a trail close to the ocean. It was windy and a bit cold. The trail was close to a busy highway, a port, and a ferry causeway. I had been there many times before, but it was the first time since the surgery. I was fine, and then suddenly, I was sobbing. I was overwhelmed by fear. Dumitru had no idea what happened, and I did not tell him as I did not know how to explain it. We went back to the car. I thought I was losing my mind.

In time, I realized I would suddenly start crying if I heard a loud and unexpected noise. Seeing an ambulance or a fire truck in the distance was fine, but if they came toward me with sirens on, it would set me off in a panic. When I started speech therapy, I did fine when asked yes or no questions, but my sessions would always end with me sobbing uncontrollably for no reason. The therapist was very kind; she would adjust my emotional reactions to the exercises. It was months later that I realized I was unable to read.

Over the summer of 2019, I continued with physiotherapy and saw improvements. At the same time, the stress of my breathing issues and upcoming laryngology surgery did not help. The surgery was successful, and I had started seeing friends again, but I continued to have sudden outbursts of crying for no apparent reason.

My family doctor saw me in August 2019. I had been visiting his office frequently since the sent surgery for check-ups, and I was usually upbeat and happy to talk about my physical recovery. However, this time, I did not want to talk to him. The doctor spoke to me about the fact that it is not unusual to feel emotional after a major health issue. I broke down in tears and told him about the night after my first surgery. This was the first time Dumitru had heard about it. I said that waking up that night was a terrifying experience as I only remembered going to bed with a migraine. It was hard to explain as I was not afraid of dying or being physically hurt; it was more visceral than that. I felt pure fear—intense and all-consuming. I would try to block it out, push it away, or down into my gut, but I could not. The tears would suddenly stream, and I could not stop them. Logically, I knew I was safe and out of danger; my health was constantly improving. However, when I was startled by something, my logic went out the window. I did not want to feel the fear anymore; I thought I was going mad. The doctor talked to us about post-traumatic stress disorder (PTSD) and referred me to a counsellor with PTSD experience. I had known my family doctor for almost 19 years. I felt comfortable with him, but the idea that I would have to now talk about my fears with an unknown man terrified me. The doctor realized something was wrong and referred me to a female counsellor.

Understanding that I was not going mad helped, but breaking down the barriers and talking about it with someone was much harder. What helped me most was my desire to get better. I spent months identifying the key triggers and learning to relax and let go. I understood that recovery is a long process with ups and downs and successes one day and sometimes regressions the next. I learned a lot from my first counsellor, Midge. I was very vulnerable, but I was also very receptive to what she suggested I try. Some people do not find group therapy and talk therapy difficult. This was not easy for me, and the counsellor helped me a great deal with Eye Movement Desensitization and Reprocessing (EMDR) therapy and bilateral stimulation music instead of talk therapy. Within weeks, I had fewer flashbacks and could recover faster if I was startled by something. However, as I got stronger, I also retreated into my own shell. I realized that it was easier for me to talk about my physical improvement and found ways to deflect any in-depth conversations. It was easier for me to project the image of doing well overall and, physically, I continued to improve. I had learned some relaxation techniques and assumed that I would not need more counselling sessions. I did not realize at the time that these sessions had stopped being effective, as I was not doing the emotional and mental recovery work needed.

As I worked through my physical recovery and re-learning how to read, spell, and write, I received a jury duty summons in July 2020. For the first time in more than a year, I felt I could deal with the request independently rather than have Dumitru sort it out for me. However, my first mistake was not reading the letter correctly. The letter provided a website and email address response option, but I only saw the phone number and focused on it rather than the entire letter. As I dialled the number, I got very nervous. The first thing the woman on the other end of the line asked for was a fifteen-to-twenty-digit ID. Right away, I realized this was going to be a challenge, as even familiar numbers, like my home number, were hard to read. I tried, but I did not get too far as fear suddenly rose in me, and I experienced a flashback. I do not remember much of the rest of the call.

Dumitru was home and heard me crying. By the time he came to me, the woman had hung up. Her voice was sympathetic, but I could not stop crying. Afterwards, I felt she had been more distressed than I. The next day, a letter arrived by courier with my jury duty exemption. This was when I knew I needed to seek the help of a psychologist.

Some brain injury or stroke survivors navigate the emotional recovery quickly and easily. Others need more time. Some people only need brief support from family or friends. Others can benefit from professional support: a family doctor, a counsellor, a brain injury support group, a psychologist. We all encounter challenges in our life journey, some small and some big. I generally felt strong because I had believed from a young age that no one else would save me; I had to take care of what I could control. When I was eight, in 1977, I lived through a violent earthquake (7.5 magnitude on the Richter scale). Our house was damaged, and our elementary school and other buildings were flattened to the ground. Around two thousand people died. When I was seventeen, in 1986, a similar earthquake hit the same area. There were fewer casualties, but it was still a very frightening experience. Both earthquakes occurred after dark. There was never any support for those affected. The families and communities did their best to recover on their own, as the communist regime did not acknowledge what happened, with the newspapers and TV stations heavily censored. After the stent surgery, I needed to process a lot of sensations, feelings, and emotions. I was used to suppressing them to continue to survive and exist without falling apart. I wanted to continue to deflect these emotions, lock them away, and pretend they never existed. However, when I woke up from the stent surgery, it seemed that I was no longer able to control them. The raw fear, memories, and sensations were too strong for me to ignore. I needed the support of a psychologist that could see beyond the façade I was so used to hiding behind. And this time, I was ready to accept the support.

Finding a therapist with the necessary experience to provide effective treatment is very personal. Everyone has their unique style, and some people are less social than others, especially after suffering a brain injury. Each therapist brings their own professional and life experience to the table, and it is important to get a sense of the connection with one's therapist. I trusted Dumitru, my family doctor, and my counsellor. However, I was not ready to open up about my fears and memories until I connected with Dr. Bea Mackay. She is a trained psychologist who has extensive PTSD and EMDR experience and could relate to family life in the 1970s.

The key is not to get discouraged. Keep trying until you find a therapist you feel is right for you. Then keep working through your new way of being in the post-brain injury world. The brain needs to develop new neural pathways. Like physical therapy, I am learning that time and patience are necessary with emotional recovery and that healing is a journey of self-discovery and cannot be rushed. I am learning to know that some days are harder than others; that it gets better slowly; that one day, you will be stronger than the previous day; and keep asking for help when needed. For family and friends, it is important to know that just being there helps. Sometimes, solely listening or gently encouraging the brain injury survivors helps them know they are not alone on this journey.

SPEECH THERAPY

From the beginning of my hospital stay at Vancouver General Hospital, Dumitru was with me daily, from 7 a.m. to 8 p.m. Since he worked from home as an IT consultant with mostly US-based clients, he had always had a flexible schedule. He worked from the hospital on his laptop when I would sleep during the day. Sometimes he had to attend meetings on his cell phone, when he would go to his car in the hospital parking lot. However, most of the time, he was by my bedside.

A few days after my stent surgery, I spent time in a shared room with four to six others after I was moved from the ICU. Dumitru brought my iPod so that I could listen to music and audiobooks. I seldom talked, only answering the nurses' and doctors' questions when asked. A therapist came in for an assessment and asked me a few questions. First, she asked me to look at some pictures and point to the correct image. Then, she asked me to look at the pictures and name the items—flower, floor, window. Then she pointed to different objects in the room and asked me to name them—chair, table, cup. The only thing I could not name was her car keys as she pulled them from her pocket. I knew what they were; I just could not name them. The woman did not explain anything, and I never saw her again. However, she seemed happy with how I was doing.

I was then moved into a private room. Dumitru brought me my iPhone so that I could have access to more apps. I was always a fast and avid reader. I was so happy to finally read the news that I did not notice anything was wrong as I read to myself. Since I tired easily, I only read the CBC news for 5-10 minutes at a time. At this point, there was a measles outbreak at the hospital, and I followed the pro and anti-vaccination stories with interest. Coming from a dictatorship, I was surprised to learn that Canadian parents can opt out of having their children vaccinated due to potential side effects. The pros and cons of the arguments were interesting, and they took my mind off things. Before my stroke, I would skip the adverts and scan the information quickly as I was always busy, so I still did not notice that anything was wrong with my reading as I continued to do this. I now also had a TV in my room, and I watched movies and the local news, never noticing any issues as I managed to follow what was on TV and listen to my audiobooks.

When I was finally released from the hospital many days after my brain injury, I spent two days at Surrey Memorial Hospital. Before being discharged, I had a final assessment, and this was when I was told that I had a major hurdle to overcome. The therapists assessing me assumed that I was fine as I spoke English very well. We knew that the stroke caused by artery dissection had seriously affected my language center as I had a tough time speaking Romanian. However, my English was fine, or so I thought. The therapists brought a laptop into my room and asked me to type my first and last name and a short phrase, like "Today is a sunny day." That is when we all realized that I could not even type my first and last name. It turned out that I had lost the ability to spell, and I would need to see a speech-language pathologist. While waiting, I tried to respond to friends and work colleagues who had sent flowers and cards. Since I am right-handed and my right hand and arm were paralyzed, I could not write, so I tried emailing. I quickly realized that it was not possible as I could not spell in English or Romanian. Dumitru wrote a few emails on my behalf as I did not want people to know I was so ill.

After three weeks at home, I started outpatient therapy at the Peace Arch Hospital in White Rock, BC.

Many months later, I learned that Speech-Language Pathology (SLP) is a broad field of expertise. People who suffer brain injuries are often referred to an SLP outpatient program to assess speech, language, and swallowing disorders. This may include communication and reading issues. Without knowing more about SLP at the time, I assumed I would work with an SLP therapist to help me with my inability to spell in English.

When I met the SLP therapist, she completed an assessment. We started with easy exercises that required me to only provide yes/no answers. Then we moved onto exercises that required me to read some material on my own, and I had to tell her, in my own words, what the story was about. She was trying to assess my reasoning, attention, and memory skills. I had no problem recounting the details. Then we moved on to some exercises that required me to name things like any animals I could think of. There was a time limit, but I managed to name many animals in quick succession, so the therapist was pleased.

Then we moved on to a more complex exercise. The therapist asked me to read a paragraph aloud, and I started to cry. After the stent surgery, I often started crying, unable to explain what was wrong to Dumitru, the doctors, or other therapists. I often felt that my brain was in slow motion and, although I understood things, I had a hard time processing complex information. For example, I had difficulty eating after coming home from the hospital; I had no appetite. I also had facial paralysis and therefore lacked strength in my jaw. When Dumitru would prepare meals, I sometimes acted like a toddler, crying uncontrollably, unable to state that I only wanted a small portion as eating was difficult. I felt the same way when the SLP therapist asked me to read aloud. Unfortunately, the therapist did not explain what was wrong with my reading ability. Instead, she simply asked me to paraphrase the content, which was easy for me to do.

I do not recall having any discussions with the SLP therapist about the assessment results or discussing any issues, challenges, or goals I might have regarding reading. We simply agreed that I would attend weekly sessions over the next few weeks.

The sessions lasted about 45 minutes, and we never spoke about reading aloud again. Each time we met, I was happy to see that the exercises involving attention, memory, and focus were easy. However, I was rattled because speaking English was easy, but not knowing why and how I could spell certain words and not others was a mystery, which frustrated me. I realized that I could not spell the days of the week, the months of the year, or simple words like who, what, when, where, why, or how. I still could not spell my first and last name, Dumitru's name, or my friends' names, making it more evident that I was in serious trouble. Before my brain injury, my job involved writing and reviewing business cases and managerial reports and responding to 50 to 100 emails per day, in-between attending or facilitating meetings and teaching and training project managers. I had no idea how I would return to my job without any command of spelling.

Unfortunately, the SLP therapist did not explain much, and I was too tired and overwhelmed to ask questions. In my mind, I knew that I did not need an English teacher as my spoken English was fine, but the therapist did not tell me that I would need to re-learn how to spell most English words. She also did not explain what was going on in my mind. My first months of spelling attempts looked like this: "I ud like a tee, pleez," meaning: "I would like a tea, please." Instead of explaining the problem to me, the therapist would simply correct my spelling on the iPad we used.

Early in my recovery, Dumitru and I took a walk in a local park to see the blooms, and I became interested in the names of the plants. At the same time, I was checking my Romanian spelling. Some common plant names were easy to spell in Romanian, but I could only remember the English names for some. Tulips were easy to spell, but daffodils were not. Snowdrops did not make any sense. I could spell rhododendron, but I did not understand why I knew how to spell this particular word.

I could spell "land," but I could not spell "island;" "other" was fine, "another" was a mystery. I wished that someone had told me about prefixes and suffixes, as my brain could not process that at the time. I realized that some words finish in terminations, such as "tion," "sion," etc., so I began to look up similar words with the same suffixes.

After a few weeks, the SLP therapist asked if I would try SLP group therapy that included two other female patients. Since the group was small, I agreed.

At the first session, we were asked to fill in a form and answer a list of short questions to support the conversation. I got anxious immediately as I saw that the two other patients had no issues with writing. I could not write with my right hand as it was paralyzed, so I was asked to use my left hand. I still remember some of the questions: "What is your favourite trip?" "What is your favourite city?" "What is your favourite hobby?" We were given some time to write, but I was quickly overwhelmed as I could not spell any words I wanted to write. I was also terrified because I realized that I would be asked to talk in front of the group. The ladies took their time to answer. One was accompanied by her husband as she needed help remembering things. Both were nice and easy-going. When my turn came, I burst into tears. I was so embarrassed! I also felt guilty because the others seemed very uncomfortable with my crying. I did not continue and remained silent for the rest of the session. When the session was over, Dumitru talked to the SLP therapist and the outpatient program supervisor, and they agreed that I would not attend any more SLP group therapy sessions.

During the initial weeks of the SLP therapy sessions at the outpatient hospital, I looked for stroke and brain recovery books. I searched for options online and found an audiobook titled *My Stroke of Insight* by Jill Bolte Taylor, Ph.D. I asked the SLP therapist about the book, and after a week, she showed me a copy of it. Even though I was unaware that I had a reading problem, I decided I would purchase the audiobook rather than the printed copy, and I found it very helpful. The author explained a lot more about the brain, spelling, and communication. I remember wishing the therapist had done so.

At the end of May 2019, I learned that my SLP therapist was changing jobs. At the time, I was dealing with my upcoming laryngology surgery, so we agreed I would not continue with the program. I mentioned the Tactus Therapy app she was using at the hospital during our session and asked if I could buy it. She gave me the name of the app. We bought it online, and I was thrilled to continue using it on my own. As we finished the sessions, the therapist advised me not to worry too much about spelling as most people cannot spell anyway. This was not the advice I was looking for as I was increasingly concerned about returning to work. As a knowledge worker, I could not comprehend how I would function without spelling and writing in the workplace. Knowing I had the Tactus Therapy app made me feel more comfortable. However, I still did not know that I was having significant issues with reading.

Dealing with numbers was very hard too. I recognized the digits if I saw them on paper or a screen, but I would say the wrong number aloud. I realize now that my issue with reading aloud should have been addressed much sooner. However, this was only evident to me eight months after my surgery, when an experienced SLP therapist finally confirmed I had a reading issue and that learning how to deal with numbers was a part of it.

In hindsight, it would have helped to have had a detailed assessment with another SPL therapist, one that could navigate my emotional state while properly understanding and offering a recovery plan suited to my needs. All the SLP therapists I have met to date were born in Canada. I am unsure whether they realized the challenge I was facing as an immigrant. I spoke English well, yet I had lost most of my native language. I could read and paraphrase accurately, with great focus and no memory issues, but I would burst into tears when asked to read aloud. After the first two weeks following my brain injury, I had begun to read the news online, yet I recognized much later that I was skimming the context to get the meaning and not actually reading. I did not know who to ask for advice as my brain could not make sense of what was going on. I felt like I was trying to solve a puzzle with many missing pieces.

In the absence of a better recovery plan, I spent the summer of 2019 re-learning how to spell the days of the week and the months of the year. Next, I learned to spell names. Ed was easy; Michael was very hard. I eventually learned how to spell my name (Laura) in English and Romanian.

The six questions (who, what, when, where, why, how) were difficult for me, but many exercises involved them. I wish someone would have explained why I was having so much difficulty with this.

Words related to timing or relativity were a mystery. The words "before," "after," "under," "above," "underline" were incredibly frustrating. I could arrange or rearrange the objects on my Tactus Therapy app correctly, but I could not get certain pictures right. For example, the picture would show a woman and a man running, and the app would asked me to correctly identify the answer: "She is leading; she is led by him; he is following." I never got these examples right.

I still did not know what or who to look for. I learned English in Romania at school with no instruction beyond the classes where I took one hour of instruction per week from Grades 5 to 12. At the time, we learned words mechanically, with a lot of repetition and almost no conversation. I loved to read, and by the time I received a summer scholarship in Ann Arbor, Michigan, when I was 22 years old, I spoke well enough to be accepted into the program. Then I got a job with a large management consulting firm in Romania, and all my work was in English. I became fluent in English, but I never learned the language in a structured way, so I did not know the reasoning behind some of the grammatical structures or rules for spelling. So, after my surgery, I did not know how I knew English; I just spoke it. However, whenever I realized that I could not spell the words I had spoken, I would get overwhelmed. Not knowing how it was possible to talk and not spell was hard. In the first months, things continued to feel in slow motion. I was exhausted and sometimes discouraged as my brain needed to process too many things at once.

One of my close friends, Carla, is a Montessori teacher, and we talked a bit in the first few weeks after I came home from the hospital. When I saw her for the second time, we talked about the exercises I was doing for my hand therapy and realized parallels between the things I was being told in physiotherapy that resonated with the Montessori principles. While the recovery of my hand motor skills was the first area addressed in physiotherapy, I remember Carla explaining to me how young children in Montessori schools learn skills for everyday life, like tying shoes, buttoning a shirt, and pouring water. At the time, I was focused on recovering my right-hand function, not realizing how beneficial these conversations would be later. Our visits were short as I was either busy with other therapy sessions or was tired, and she was busy with her job.

Both my initial speech therapist and Carla had been taught differently from how I learned English, so it was hard for them to understand my challenges, and it was hard for me to explain. Carla and I talked about how difficult it was for me to "sound" letters out. There were so many sounds and so many rules ("eye," "I," "flight," "high," "light," "oat," "boat," "vote," "move," "food," "rude," "rule"). She helped me with an auditory drill using a set of cards to determine which sounds were hard for me. Then she printed pages from a phonetics reference guide, and I started practicing the short vowels, long vowels, and the sounds that were difficult for me ("ch-," "qu-," "-tch," "-dge," "-ge," etc.). Although she was not a speech therapist, she helped me more than all the SLP therapists combined as she understood that I needed to learn how to sound the letters out as I was trying to re-learn how to spell.

In the first months at the gym, the trainers would often explain things two or three times. At first, some assumed I was hard of hearing as I would not understand their verbal instructions. In time, I learned that I needed them to "show" me and then I understood. For example, they would need to show me how to do a lunge or wall push-up rather than using words. I knew something was wrong with my ability to understand words in certain contexts, but I did not know how to explain that to the trainers.

This kept me busy over the summer. In addition, Carla and I talked about writing as I wanted to write again. She gave me several Canadian Handwriting workbooks and printed off a few of the first letters of the alphabet. I could not hold a pen until late summer, but once I could, I started repeatedly writing each letter of the alphabet, beginning with A. The practice and repetition made sense, and I could see the results as I continued my sessions.

Over the summer, I also continued with the Tactus Therapy app. I used it mainly for spelling at first, then I upgraded the app to more modules and realized I could practice more things. I started playing with the more complex writing module. However, I never opened the reading module, even though I had seen the module on the app.

In September 2019, I needed to take a few voice therapy sessions following my throat surgery. This was a very interesting experience. I always had a soft voice, and I felt I needed some help as my voice was strained, and people had a hard time hearing me. In my mind, this therapy was no different than physiotherapy, so I was not concerned at all. My hand physiotherapist recommended me to a colleague of hers, an SLP therapist who specialized in voice issues. The therapist, Sherri, began the assessment by talking to me about the concerns I had with my voice, and then we started. She gave me a page with about ten lines written on it. She told me to read each line so that she could hear my voice. This was when I first realized I could not read aloud. I felt just like when I realized I could not spell my first name. I started crying. I felt terrible. All my fears and years of feeling like I was never safe and never good enough came rushing in. Oh my God, I was illiterate! I felt ignorant, foolish, and ashamed.

Sherri was kind and had the experience to handle the situation well. She allowed me to collect myself. Then she took the time to explain that it was not uncommon for people who had had brain injuries to have reading issues, although she admitted to not having realized it in me since I spoke fine. She quickly explained that this did not mean

I was ignorant; I just needed to understand that I had suffered a brain injury and that I was still the same person I was before the stent surgery. The words gradually sank in. Logically, I understood what she said. I then realized that when I was in the hospital after my first surgery, I watched TV and listened to audiobooks, so it made sense that I could understand everything.

For the first time, someone took the time to help me understand that I had a major issue rather than finding ways around it. I now wondered why my first SLP therapist did not assess my reading. She must have realized I had reading issues, so why did she not tell me? Maybe she felt I was too emotional at the first assessment? Maybe she wanted to bring it up later in therapy? I will never know.

Sherri adjusted the exercises to my needs, and I completed the assessment and a set of voice therapy sessions without being asked to read aloud.

With the new knowledge I had about my reading issues, I started looking for another SLP therapist. I wanted to try a different approach because I did not want to be told again not to worry about my spelling. SLP therapists specializing in adult reading seem to be rare. I worked with one SLP therapist specializing in childhood dyslexia for a couple of sessions, which was very informative. By that time, however, I had learned a lot of what I needed on my own and not enough of what I still wanted to learn, so I continued looking for other options. At the same time, I had started to use the reading module of the Tactus Therapy app. I began with the very easy stories—2-3 lines. I had to practice reading aloud, away from Dumitru, as I could not bear for him to hear me. I knew I sounded like a first grader. Things got easier, and I mastered the first level in a few weeks.

In October 2019, I accidentally came across a brain injury recovery group at the gym I had started to attend in May 2019. This was a local group, the Delta Stroke Recovery Society, located in my hometown in Tsawwassen. I connected with the group and set up a meeting to speak to an SLP therapist. The initial assessment was difficult as I had to admit, once again, that I could not read. I attended two sessions there. The first consisted of only four participants. I realized I was the only one in the group who had issues with reading and spelling, but they were very supportive and kind, and the session went well.

The following week, I was asked to join a larger group (14-16 people). We sat in a u-shape around a table, with everyone taking turns talking about Halloween memories. I should have left, but I froze instead. When it was my turn, I started talking and dissolved in tears within seconds. It took me about half an hour to recover from crying. I did not want to go back again as I was very embarrassed and felt I had upset the other participants. They were all very nice, and I later realized it was my issue, not theirs.

It took me months of PTSD therapy to realize what was triggering me. Having lived in a communist dictatorship in Romania, I knew that I could not talk to people about my family as it was unsafe. So, I learned to be quiet or only make small talk. I was a natural observer, and I preferred to be unheard and unseen if possible. For years, I did not like to have any attention on me, so I would avoid spontaneous activities. After my brain injury, I had developed social anxiety after being put on the spot in group therapy sessions that highlighted my inability to spell, write, and read. So, I resolved never to try speech therapy in a group setting again.

However, I knew I needed to keep trying to get help to address my SLP needs. I contacted the Delta Stroke Recovery Society coordinator, Susan, and asked her to put me in touch with the SLP lead therapist via email. Susan connected me with Shari, and Shari connected me with Vera, one of her most experienced team members, and we completed an assessment. Even though I still shed tears, Vera explained to me more about my reading difficulties in one hour than I learned from all the other SLPs I had met in the past eight months!

In the next few sessions, I learned about alexia and acquired dyslexia. I received links to articles that gave me answers and ideas to try for my recovery. Vera recommended I read *The Man Who Forgot How to Read* by Howard Engel. This gave me the courage to go to the local library and renew my library card. Anyone who has had their dominant hand affected by a brain injury or a physical injury can relate to the difficulty of signing a card with a pen that is not kind to weak fingers. At Vera's advice, I told the librarian that I had a brain injury and asked for help.

This was the first time I felt comfortable telling a stranger about my brain injury and asking for help. The librarian helped me as the book search system seemed strange to me.

The book by Howard Engel is short, yet I had a hard time reading it as I was still reading like a small child; I had to re-read each sentence a few times to make sure I understood. I needed two library extensions to finish the book, but it motivated me to continue reading as I was very interested in learning about the author's story.

I continued to see Vera throughout 2020 and into 2021. Focusing on what was relevant for me was very important. Bringing up my reading concerns helped, as I was dealing with several other therapies at the same time. I finally understood that reading aloud in public or trying to take down notes in a telephone conversation (listening on the phone, writing down the spelling, and making sure I did not make mistakes with the addresses, phone numbers, or times for appointments) was more to do with social anxiety than my ability to read. Learning to relax and rediscovering reading for fun is an ongoing process. Listening to audiobooks is still convenient, especially since I do a lot of walking. However, being able to read is very important to me, so I continue to practice. Like spelling and writing, I feel that reading is part of my identity, and it is important for me to read aloud and, one day, go back to presenting, training, and teaching as part of my work.

The speech therapy journey was arduous. Speaking different languages, living in other cultures, experiencing past traumas, and my brain injury all contributed to making it difficult for me to find the right path toward recovery. Many brain injury survivors speak other languages outside of English or French in Canada. My journey was difficult as I did not know how to explain what I needed. Being able to speak English well but having to re-learn how to spell from scratch took an emotional toll on me.

I was so focused on my English spelling, reading, and writing that I did not place much attention on my Romanian. However, the more Dumitru and I spent time walking together, the more I spoke Romanian. While struggling to figure out what I needed to recover my English spelling, I paid attention to the things that did not work in my native language. Romanian is a Romance language. As such, Romanian nouns are either feminine, masculine, or neutral. They also require proper declination (singular or plural). The articles, adjectives, and pronouns must agree in gender, number, and case with the noun they modify. In English, "red" is still "red," whether it is an adjective or a noun. For example, a "*red* ball," a "*red* truck." English is simple and straightforward that way. In Romanian, a "*red* ball" becomes "minge *rosie*," a "*red* truck" becomes "camionul *rosu*." No wonder I could not speak my native language properly. It took many months for me to speak better in Romanian, and it was gradual. An SLP specialist with linguistics expertise might have been able to explain what was happening. However, whether it was a matter of practice or the gradual recovery of my brain neuroplasticity, I made good progress by continuing to talk to Dumitru and other Romanian friends. As hard as it was for me to regain my native language, Romanian spelling is much easier than English spelling, so I managed to recover my Romanian spelling within a few weeks. However, my English spelling improvements took more that two years!

The key is not to get discouraged and keep trying to find an SLP therapist who can eventually help you. Staying motivated helped me reach my first goals. Although it was hard for many months, once I knew I was on the right path, it became easier to see results and trust that I would recover.

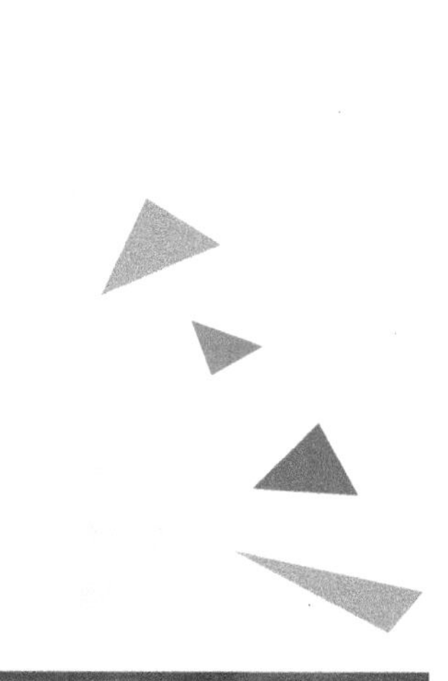

vine glasses mn u v w y

WARM-UP DRILLS

Monday
Tuesday
Wednesday
Thursday
Friday
Saturday
Sunday

One
Two
Three
Four
Five
Six
Seven
Eight
Nine
Ten

Eleven
Twelve
Thirteen
Fourteen
Fifteen
Sixteen
Seventeen
Eighteen
Nineteen
Twenty

Baranof Island (US)
Sardinia (Italy)
Magdalen Island (Canada)
Jeju (South Korea)
Arozes (Portugal)
Falkland Island (Great Britain)
Majuli (India)
New Caledonia (France)
Chiloe (Chile)
Lofoten Island (Norway)
Guataloupe (France)
Bocas del Toro (Panama)
Great Barrier Island (New Zealand)
Reunion Island (France)
Monserrat (Great Britain)
Bali (Indonesia)
Faroe Island (Denmark)
Salt Spring (Canada)
Crete (Greece)
Newfoundland (Canada)
Cuba
Okinawa (Japan)
Cape Verde
Channel Islands (Great Britain)

VOICE THERAPY

Apart from the challenges I faced when I finally realized I had a hard time reading, I had problems with my voice after the intubation surgery. I always had a soft voice, but I rarely had vocal issues. People often noted that I needed to speak up, but I did not like to be loud. I had had laryngitis once in my life and lost my voice completely for a few days, but this was different.

After the laryngeal surgery, everything was fine structurally. I did not talk a lot during the day, and my voice became hoarse in time. It was a vicious cycle, in a way. For months after my brain injury, I did not want to talk to people on the phone; I preferred that Dumitru speak for me. On the rare occasion that I did pick up the phone, I would quickly pass it to Dumitru, as in most cases, I needed to write down details—appointment details, names, phone numbers—and I could not. I often ended up in tears, not wanting to talk to anyone.

When we went out in public in 2019, I often had a hard time when we would run into friends, especially if the places were loud or noisy. I mostly avoided going out.

The voice clinic helped me get past these challenges. I recommend that anyone who has had a brain injury and their voice has been affected see a qualified speech-language pathologist (SLP) specializing in voice therapy. After my initial assessment with Sherri, I was advised to follow a series of voice exercises for three to four sessions. The semi occluded vocal tract exercises involved simple actions like using a straw, humming, changes in voice pitch, revving and singing, or reading aloud. As I was uncomfortable reading aloud, Sherri recorded me as she asked me to repeat a few short sentences, and then I just had to listen to the sentences and repeat them aloud.

I practiced the exercises twice a day, two times through, with 1-2 minutes of rest in between. Within a few sessions, my friends noted that my voice was much stronger, and I started to enjoy talking more. I practiced the exercises for 3-4 months, and my confidence improved significantly. At the same time, I was engaged in more therapy sessions, and in February 2020, I realized that my voice was almost back to normal. In March 2020, as the pandemic restrictions started, I noticed that my voice was getting hoarse again, so I went back to the voice exercises. This was a good reminder that I needed to use my voice more.

As I continue my recovery journey, I'm beginning to understand that our voice is connected to our emotions. Before my brain injury, I was good at hiding my emotions. For the first twenty years of my life, I felt I had no voice and was not safe. People often told me that I was very calm and collected even as my heart pounded in my chest. I was conditioned to hide my feelings and emotions, push things down, and focus on the task at hand. Staying safe was my priority, not my voice.

After my brain injury, I often did not want to talk to others because I felt my voice would betray me. When I would get overwhelmed, my voice would falter first, and then the tears would come. When my fears came up, I would hold my breath for as long as possible. Then I would go from tears to crying inconsolably in seconds.

As my voice becomes physically stronger, and as I learn more therapy techniques to get more comfortable with emotions, I am gradually finding my voice. I would like to give other brain injury survivors a voice as well. We identify ourselves in many ways without thinking too much about it. If you feel that your voice has been affected by a brain injury, finding a voice clinic is a good place to start.

IT TAKES A VILLAGE

At the beginning of my recovery, Dumitru and I often felt lost as we learned to deal with the healthcare system. I received excellent care from the Vancouver General Hospital for three weeks. I was supported by wonderful doctors, nurses, and therapists as I went through stent surgery and was stabilized. I felt I had a strong team around me. Then I was transferred to another hospital for further recovery services, and that transfer proved to be difficult to navigate.

As my brain was gradually coming back online, I was struck by the sense that we were alone and had to figure everything out by ourselves. I was discharged from Surrey Memorial Hospital within two days, without an opportunity to connect with the staff, and I never heard from anyone in that team again. Over the next three to four months, the Peach Arch Hospital outpatient program provided services. However, the small team did not refer me to any brain injury or stroke recovery group in my community. Eight months later, I discovered the Delta Stroke Recovery Society of BC in my hometown in Tsawwassen, two miles from my house. I also learned about the Richmond Stroke Recovery Centre of BC, eleven miles away, and the Vancouver GF Strong Rehabilitation Centre of BC, seventeen miles away, both closer to our home than where I was sent to after being transferred from VGH.

Health authorities may not necessarily look at the patient's best interest if one lives at the edge of the geographical boundaries. I live closer to VGH than Surrey Memorial Hospital or Peace Arch Hospital, yet I was transferred to Fraser Health Authority hospitals, further away and unfamiliar to me.

Brain injury survivors have to deal with many issues, but a lack of information and support should not be one of them. I believe there should be a better way to serve patients in a way that places the patients at the centre of the recovery, with access to necessary information and resources faster and easier. This includes access to brain recovery outpatient services available locally or in nearby communities. I still get all my medical follow-up services at VGH or in Vancouver. I should at least have been given a choice of outpatient services in the Vancouver Coastal Health Authority.

Accessibility to resources is critical in recovery success. Brain injury survivors should be discharged from the acute care hospital with a list of available recovery groups and therapists in their area. If it is necessary to transfer patients to another hospital, a proper handover between hospitals should occur to ensure that adequate communication is in place and that the patient or their family has an opportunity to review the handover plan and address any questions that may come up.

Time is of the essence after a brain injury, not only during emergency care but also while waiting for outpatient services. Patients and family or friends can explore the resources, understand the options, and make informed decisions about locations that work best for them. The patient should be made aware of options for extended health care insurance if available. When a limb is affected by a stroke, and paralysis or weakness occurs, patients may experience weakness, stiffness, change in sensation or lack of sensation. Starting physiotherapy or occupational therapy as soon as possible is very important, as waiting for weeks or months for outpatient services can make the recovery more difficult.

Recovery takes teamwork from doctors, nurses, therapists, rehabilitation program coordinators, family, and friends. Having a strong advocate, like a family or friend, is very important to help with navigating the healthcare system, talking with doctors and therapists, keeping track of appointments, and driving the patient to therapy sessions. An advocate can also offer emotional support and encouragement. I was fortunate to find excellent support in Dumitru, who cheered me on, stood by me, encouraged me, and advocated on my behalf when I felt like giving up.

Our healthcare system is not perfect, and it can be frustrating to try to navigate through. I would encourage persistence. I learned in time to recognize when a healthcare provider or therapist is not a good fit for me. This does not mean that the therapist is not experienced enough or not qualified enough; it just means that the connection is not there. If you are not comfortable with their approach or feel your needs are not met, I encourage you to look for another therapist.

Recovery resources are often scattered and require patience to sift through to find what is relevant to your case. In Canada, Brain Injury Canada (www.braininjurycanada.ca), the Heart and Stroke Foundation (www.heartandstroke.ca), and the After Stroke organization (www.afterstroke.ca) have excellent websites to get you started on your journey. Provincial and local recovery groups also provide very good online resources to support your recovery.

Although I had a hard time believing it at first, I can say from personal experience that things get easier and better. My physical recovery is almost complete. I take long walks every day, rain or shine. I continue to practice my fine motor skills in day-to-day activities that I enjoy. I play tennis again; I can serve, and my double backhand is strong. I enjoy drawing and colouring and have fun learning to play the piano. I continue to practice reading aloud, and I know that one day, I will be confident enough to share my knowledge and skills with others, something I used to really enjoy. My handwriting is better now than it was before! I am making slow but steady progress on my PSTD journey and hope that I will be able to return to work one day.

Staying aware of your body and mind is essential. You will see the small changes that lead to a step up and forward in your recovery if you pay attention. Learning to slow down and to breathe is becoming easier. Taking it one day at a time is a truly valuable lesson—one I had a hard time with. By staying hopeful and embracing the journey, I believe that I will be fully recovered one day soon, and

I will not just be a brain injury survivor. I will be thriving and enjoying what I learned from my experience and sharing it with others, and I will continue to grow physically, emotionally, and intellectually. I have always admired wise people—my grandmother, some family and friends, teachers, philosophers, and writers. Before my brain injury, I assumed some people were wise, and I was not. I now believe that I am on the right path of the wisdom journey too, not as an end goal or finite state of mind, but as a daily practice in pursuit of more learning and sharing. And if I can do it, so can you, one day at a time, on a journey of hope, living life with grace and ease.

APPENDIX

Below are some valuable resources I came across in my recovery:

BOOKS

My Stroke of Insight by Jill Bolte Taylor, Ph. D.

Relentless—How a Massive Stroke Changed My Life for the Better by Ted W. Baxter

The Brain That Changes Itself by Norman Doidge, MD

The Man Who Forgot How to Read by Howard Engle

Daydreams—Coloring Book Illustrated by Hanna Karizon

NETFLIX (DOCUMENTARY)

My Beautiful Broken Brain—Lotje Sodderland

APPLICATIONS

Tactus Therapy (www.tactustherapy.com)

RECOVERY ORGANIZATIONS

Brain Injury Canada (www.braininjurycanada.ca)

Heart and Stroke Foundation (www.heartandstroke.ca)

After Stroke (www.afterstroke.ca)

After Stroke BC Virtual Programs (www.strokerecoverybc.ca)

BC Brain Wellness Program (www.bcbrainwelness.ca)

Delta Stroke Recovery Society (www.deltastrokerecovery.com)

ACKNOWLEDGEMENTS

To the Delta, BC Fire Department crew that came to our house quickly and provided assessment and assistance, thank you!

Thank you to the Delta, BC Ambulance Services crew, and the paramedic who determined that I had to be sent straight from home to Vancouver General Hospital (VGH) rather than taking me to the local hospital.

To the VGH emergency neurological team, to Dr. Oscar Benavente, Dr. Phillip Teal, and the neurosurgeon team, thank you for making quick and excellent decisions when my life was in danger! And thank you for supporting and guiding Dumitru, who had to speak on my behalf as I could not make decisions for myself.

To all the nurses and staff at VGH, thank you for your excellent support, kindness, and dedication during the sixteen days I spent in your care.

Special thanks to the wonderful physiotherapist at the VGH Neurology Department, Moira, for explaining the importance of rehabilitating my arm in the first days of my recovery! Thank you for stressing how important it was to keep moving my arm and telling us that the brain can re-wire itself and create new neural pathways. You showed us the importance of repetition even though I did not feel my arm at first. Moira, your words resonated with Dumitru and me! We listened to everything you said. Thank you for teaching Dumitru and me what to work on during the three weeks at VGH. I truly believe I owe my physical recovery to your excellent start, so thank you again!

To Dr. Horst Hollinger, my family physician, thank you for your excellent care and support! After years of only coming to your office for routine check-ups, I discovered quickly that my world has changed. I needed to comprehend and deal with complex health issues, and I needed to navigate the healthcare system that was so new to me. Thank you for being patient, for listening, for supporting Dumitru and me, and for always bringing a healthy dose of humour to our appointments!

To Erin Reeds, my physiotherapist specialized in neurological rehabilitation; thank you! I am so grateful to have discovered you! Thank you for explaining the concept of creating new neural pathways, as I needed to understand what and why I needed to do to get better. Even though I encountered many other therapists on my journey, I appreciate your continued and consistent support. Thank you for always encouraging me and creating solutions to keep challenging me on my road to recovery!

To Travis Wosley, my current physiotherapist, thank you! You helped me move beyond hand therapy, and into general strengthening. You continue to teach me about neuroplasticity and the value of recreating neural pathways as I get back to my life and my day-to-day activities!

Thank you to the GRASP Program organizers, Dr. Janice Eng, Dr. Chieh-ling Yang, Seonaid Waterson, and the physiotherapists and volunteer team! I am grateful to have had the opportunity to participate in the program twice. I could not have had such an amazing recovery without your encouragement and excellent support, both in-person and virtually!

To Midge Malcolm, my first counsellor, thank you for making me comfortable with the counselling process and inviting me to explore the journey within as I took small steps to explore the realm of feelings and emotions.

To Dr. Bea Mackay, my psychologist, thank you for teaching me to breathe, how to let go and discover ways to be more present, and how to experience less fear and stress. Thank you for guiding me on the interesting journey of learning to manage less and process more. I am grateful for your support as I continue to discover a new way of being in the world!

To Shari Linde, the first speech-language pathologist who properly listened to my pleas for help, thank you! And thank you for connecting me with Vera! To Vera Kinach, thank you for your kindness and for being willing to explain things and answer my questions. I appreciated your patience as I needed time to understand and process information. Thank you for supporting me as I took the first steps to read again, and I am grateful for all the excellent speech therapy resources you provided!

To Sherri Zelazny, my speech-language pathologist specialized in voice, I will thank you first for recognizing that I had a significant problem with reading after my brain injury! I appreciate your kindness as you helped me understand that I could not read well because I suffered a brain injury, not because I was illiterate. Your practical approach allowed me to practice using my voice through the exercises you recommended. I am very grateful for helping me find my voice in more ways than one; thank you!

To my Delta Stroke Recovery Society friends, thank you! From the coordinators, therapists, volunteers to the other stroke survivors, you provide an environment that is safe, supportive, and offer informative and relevant resources. I am grateful for the connections I made, for being able to interact one-on-one and in small groups, and for knowing that you understand and can relate to my experience.

To the BC Brain Wellness Program therapists, thank you! I feel that I am in a virtual community that has a common goal: to keep our mind and bodies engaged, to keep learning new things and finding ways to move forward. I truly appreciate the program and I am very grateful for it!

To my close friends, thank you all for supporting Dumitru and me, for your words of encouragement, for dropping off meals and offering assistance, and for allowing me the space I needed when I started on my road to recovery. To my tennis friends, thank you for cheering me on as I came to the courts after a few months to try to hold my racket first, then get back into it slowly.

Thank you to Carla Hall, my friend, neighbour, and Montessori teacher! From the cards, flowers, and muffins at the hospital to the first visits at home, you were there for me! You encouraged me, gave me ideas and handwriting workbooks, and you were keen to see my progress. I learned more from your Montessori education principles than all my speech therapists combined! You provided excellent feedback as I decided to document and publish my recovery journey, and for that, I am very grateful; thank you!

To Sandy Neufeld, you provided extensive feedback and helped me organize my thoughts in several key chapters of this book. You encouraged me to open up and speak my truth, and I am so grateful for that; thank you!

To Tereza Racekova, my wonderful editor, thank you for encouraging me to document my recovery journey! You provided excellent advice on structuring the material and clarifying the flow. You supported me along the way patiently as I continued to make progress on my brain recovery!

To Lesley Wexler, my talented and experienced graphic designer, thank you for creating a cover design that resonates with me and bringing my pictures to life to help illustrate parts of my recovery journey. Your publishing knowledge and experience was invaluable to me; thank you!

CPSIA information can be obtained
at www.ICGtesting.com
Printed in the USA
LVHW070900131022
730613LV00008B/111